Level 2–3

MATHEMATICS
ACTIVITIES
for the Elementary Classroom
(KSAM)

Ernest L. Kern, Senior Editor

John E. Young, Associate Editor

David Munn, Project Manager

Lisa Gollihue, Designer and Illustrator

Yvonne Cronin, Typesetter

Carol Leung, Computer Specialist

CURRICULUM ASSOCIATES®, Inc.
North Billerica, MA 01862

ISBN 1-55915-992-8
©1996—Curriculum Associates, Inc.
North Billerica, MA 01862

PREFACE

Mathematics Activities for the Elementary Classroom: Level 2–3 is an outgrowth of the KSAM (**K**–6 **S**cience **A**nd **M**ath) Program, a highly successful elementary-teacher inservice program in science and mathematics that has served over 15,000 teachers since its inception in 1985 at Southeast Missouri State University. In an effort to further meet the needs of elementary teachers beyond those addressed in inservice training, KSAM conducted summer writing conferences in which educators from all levels participated, the largest group, by far, being K–6 classroom teachers. The larger number of elementary teachers was appropriate based on our belief in the old saying that the best solutions are produced by those most experienced in the problem. The charge to these educators was to develop quality, practical, affectively palatable, content-sound, process-based student activities in K–6 science and mathematics that worked well both for the teacher and the student. The result was the publication of the KSAM Mathematics Series, as well as the KSAM Biological Science Series, KSAM Earth Science Series, and KSAM Physical Science Series. Thus, the activities in all the series guides were developed *by* K–6 teachers *for* K–6 teachers. This is as it should be. For who better understands the problems and needs of the classroom teacher? Who better understands elementary students and how they think, how they learn, and how they react? Who is in a better position to develop a publication that is of maximum value to elementary teachers and their students? The answer is obviously teachers, who directly experience classroom situations each day.

The success of those educators in meeting their charge is represented by the many thousands of teachers who have successfully used the KSAM guides on a regional level prior to national publication. In fact, development of these materials within a major teacher inservice program has allowed for the repeated classroom testing and refinement of activities, resulting in a set of experiences for students that do, indeed, work well. Both success and quality are also indicated by the awards received by the KSAM Program and its math and science activity guide series, including a Meritorious Program Award (1989, U.S. Department of Education) and the Christa McAuliffe Showcase for Excellence Award (1994, American Association of State Colleges and Universities). The KSAM Program was also selected for inclusion in Promising Practices in Mathematics and Science (1994, U.S. Department of Education). Most of all, the success of these materials is mirrored in the faces of the many students who have discovered math and science to be an exciting adventure of discovery.

Mathematics Activities for the Elementary Classroom: Level 2–3 is dedicated to all elementary teachers, for without question, they are the most important element and influence in a person's total education.

Ernest L. Kern
Senior Editor

ACKNOWLEDGMENTS

It would take several pages to list, by name, all the individuals who have been involved in the development of this activity guide. Rather, let it suffice to say that deep appreciation is extended to all the elementary, secondary, and university educators who participated on the writing teams during the initial development of activities. Gratitude is also expressed to the many school districts and K–6 teachers that participated in the classroom testing of activities. Appreciation is also extended to Southeast Missouri State University, the National Science Foundation, and the Southwestern Bell Foundation, who partially supported the writing of this guide through grant funding. Finally, Nancy Pfeiffer, Staci Beussink, and Carrie Johnson deserve special mention for their dedication, loyalty, and hard work in seeing this project through.

TABLE OF CONTENTS

INTRODUCTION

Purpose

The primary purpose of the series *Mathematics Activities for the Elementary Classroom (Level K–1, Level 2–3,* and *Level 4–6)* is to provide elementary teachers with appropriate, quality materials for the enhancement of both mathematics instruction and mathematics learning in their classrooms; to aid them in their efforts to demonstrate to students not only the absolute necessity of a mathematical competency in today's society, but also the simple fact that math can be fun and exciting. Because research has so clearly shown the strong relationship between the cognitive and affective domains—that students, at all levels, learn best those things that they enjoy or find interesting or feel are important—this guide stresses the incorporation of the mathematical processes in hands-on activities that not only feature content integrity, but also elicit positive affective responses from students.

Mathematics is a required subject at every elementary level; yet, unfortunately, by the time students reach the middle school or junior high level, far too many become disenchanted with mathematics. In short, they just don't like it. It appears that much of the explanation for their "turn off" can be attributed to the nature of the subject matter itself. Mathematics is inherently abstract; however, most students at the K–6 level are in the concrete stage of mental development and thus experience difficulty thinking (or learning) in abstractions.

The activities in this guide are designed to provide students with concrete-level experiences to represent and/or supplement mathematical abstractions. In essence, the activities provide a "bridge" for the concrete thinker to better understand abstract concepts. In addition to promoting mastery of numerical skills, the activities also promote the development of the math processes, including critical thinking and reasoning, and at the same time foster interest, creativity, and enthusiasm. In short, students will find these activities to be enjoyable and exciting avenues into the numerics and processes of mathematics.

Mathematics Activities for the Elementary Classroom: Level 2–3 is not intended as a 2–3 math curriculum even though most mathematics topics covered at this level are addressed by the activities. Rather, this activity guide is specifically designed to supplement and enrich any existing curriculum.

Activity Format

The activities in this guide are written for teachers. All activities follow a standard format developed by teachers to be of maximum utilitarian value. In fact, teachers will find the activities to be much like lesson plans. The format consists of ten components.

1. **Primary Content:** identifies the major content thrust(s) of the activity.

2. **Process Skills:** lists the mathematics processes used by students in completing the activity. A complete listing of the processes, including definitions, is included in Appendix A. The processes listed under this heading will follow the same order as that presented in the appendix which, generally, runs from less complex to more complex.

3. **Prior Student Knowledge:** identifies any special knowledge, skills, or understandings needed by students to effectively complete the activity. When none are listed, normal skills and abilities for the general grade level of the activity are assumed.

4. **Group Size:** indicates the recommended size of student groups for effective learning. Entries under this heading typically fall into one of three categories: individual, groupings of various sizes, or whole class. Of course, availability of materials, class size, and teacher objectives may necessitate adjustment of the group size.

5. **Pre-Activity Preparation:** lists and describes any special materials and/or preparatory work that the teacher needs to do prior to doing the actual activity. The obtainment of typical or common materials is not included here; however, such materials are identified under the Materials Per Group heading.

6. **Materials Per Group:** a detailed listing of all materials, supplies, and equipment needed by each student group (as indicated under Group Size) for the activity. This approach makes calculating materials needed for a given activity much simpler. Whenever a listed item is intended for other than the group size previously identified in the activity, such will be indicated with that item listing. With very few exceptions, only easy-to-obtain materials are called for, usually items found in most classrooms or homes. It is assumed that every student will have pencil and paper available; those items, consequently, are usually not included in the materials listing.

7. **Teacher Information:** content information that may be needed by the teacher to fully understand the activity concept(s) and/or to effectively direct the activity in the classroom. It should be noted that this information is intended for the teacher; there is no implication that this material be wholly transferred to students. How much, if any, of the information contained in this section is presented to students is solely a decision of the teacher based upon grade level, objectives, and student abilities.

8. **Procedure:** a detailed, easy-to-follow listing of the steps necessary to set up and complete the activity. Also included for most activities are an introduction and a post-activity closure, both often in the form of suggested questioning sequences and/or discussion topics which the teacher can adapt to the appropriate student level.

9. **Extensions and Adaptations:** identifies appropriate activity extensions and adaptations to aid in the further development or reinforcement of the activity concepts.

10. **Reproducibles and Supplements:** while not listed as an individual heading, all reproducibles that accompany the activity are identified in the Pre-Activity Preparation section and the Materials Per Group section, as well as in the Procedure. Reproducibles that have specific answers are included in the Answer Key. Supplements include pages with instructions for the teacher to make items required for certain activities. Usually these pages do not need to be reproduced.

Post-Activity Closure

Educational research has long supported the fact that post-activity closure is extremely important to concept attainment. Such closure may take many forms: an informal class discussion, a specific questioning sequence, review of the activity procedure and the results or answers obtained, etc. Most of the activities in this guide contain closure to one degree or another. Frequently, when time starts running short, the "closure section" is the easiest to omit. You are encouraged to retain closure to all activities, and when possible, to expand on the suggestions presented in this guide. When time does start running short, remember that closure can always be carried over to a subsequent day.

Activity Location

In some guides, finding the right activity to supplement a given topic is quite a chore and often necessitates reviewing a number of different activities before the right one is located. *Mathematics Activities for the Elementary Classroom* incorporates several aids to help facilitate this task.

The Table of Contents groups the activities by major topics. Abbreviated Activity Descriptions follow the Introduction. These descriptions stress the content nature of the activities—usually the first concern of a teacher. The activity numbers and page numbers are also included for quick reference.

Finally, Appendix B correlates each activity to the NCTM National Mathematics Curriculum Standards that apply to the 2–3 level. Should the primary concern be the addressing of a particular standard, this appendix should prove very helpful. Activity titles are listed in order for ease of location.

NCTM National Mathematics Curriculum Standards

The National Council of Teachers of Mathematics has established a set of national standards in mathematics for all grade levels, K–12, in an effort to improve the quality of school mathematics. The NCTM curriculum standards deal primarily with content priority and emphasis, and they are divided into three categories: K–4, 5–8, and 9–12. The NCTM standards have proven to be a valuable asset to mathematics teaching, and as such, have been widely adopted nationally.

All the activities in *Mathematics for the Elementary Classroom: Level 2–3* have been correlated to NCTM curriculum standards for grades K–4. That correlation, and a listing of the standards, can be found in Appendix B, page 159.

A Word About Problem Solving

Problem solving is the principal reason for studying mathematics. Problem solving is more than the routine tasks and exercises we often spend most of our time on in the classroom. The learning of basic numerical and process skills, and the memorization of facts and rules, are all vitally important. They are the tools of mathematics that must be mastered. That is why the activities in the K–1 guide concentrate on the basic skills. Tools, however, should not be considered an end in and of themselves; they are meant to be used in a more expanded role— problem solving. Problem solving is not innate; it must be learned. Accordingly, problem solving should be an important teaching objective in those classrooms where students have mastered the basic numerical and process skills. That is why, in addition to continued work on the basic skills, problem solving appears in the 2–3 guide and takes an even more prominent role in the 4–6 guide.

For a problem to be real to a student, it must be nonroutine, understandable as a problem, and, most importantly, an acceptable challenge. While we cannot make problem solving routine, there is a loose structure or format that makes teaching problem solving a better experience for the students. Problem solving is:

1. Identifying and understanding a problem
2. Being challenged by a problem
3. Identifying needed data and ignoring unnecessary data
4. Planning a strategy to solve the problem
5. Carrying out the strategy (finding the answer)
6. Checking back to test the "fit" of the answer to the problem

Strategies to solve a given problem must be worked out by the student. However, some combination of the following may prove helpful in many problems.

1. Guess and check
2. Draw a diagram
3. Work backward through the problem
4. Work a simpler version of the problem
5. List possibilities

A Note on Safety

There is a need to be concerned about student safety in any hands-on activity in any subject. Of course, the degree of risk varies depending on the materials involved, the age and maturity level of the students, and the degree of adult supervision. Teachers sometimes think that they need only be concerned with those activities that involve heat, volatile chemicals or materials, or potentially toxic substances. However, even seemingly harmless items can become safety threats in the more open and unstructured environment that typically accompanies hands-on learning.

In utilizing the activities in this guide, you should closely supervise students at all times. In addition, you are urged to exercise caution and good judgment in all matters that might affect the safety of students. It is also recommended that if a student feels uncomfortable or sensitive about participating in a given activity, you provide an alternate experience for that student.

ABBREVIATED ACTIVITY DESCRIPTIONS

(continues)

(continued)

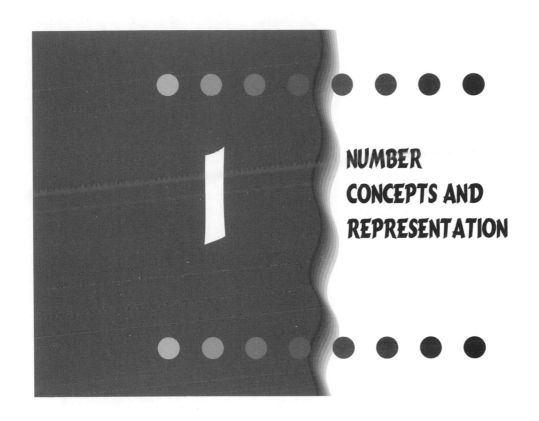

1

NUMBER CONCEPTS AND REPRESENTATION

A HANDFUL OF ODDS OR EVENS _____

PRIMARY CONTENT
Identifying odd and even numbers

PRIOR STUDENT KNOWLEDGE
Know the meaning of odd and even numbers

PRE-ACTIVITY PREPARATION
Prepare an item container for each group by placing 50–150 of the same item (beans, buttons, chips, etc.) into an open container. The container should be large enough for a student to be able to put his/her hand into the container and withdraw several items at one time.

PROCESS SKILLS
Observing, comparing, classifying, counting, matching, inferring

GROUP SIZE
2 students

MATERIALS PER GROUP
1 item container

TEACHER INFORMATION
No special teacher information is required.

PROCEDURE
1. Distribute an item container to each group.
2. For each group, place the container on a desk between the two students.
3. One student begins by reaching into the container and grasping several items.
4. The student displays the items in an open hand to the second student for a few seconds, then closes his/her hand and asks, "Is the number of items odd or is the number of items even?"
5. After the second student answers odd or even, together the two students determine what the correct answer is. The items can be lined up in rows to emphasize parity.
6. If the guess is correct, the second student gets to keep the items. If the guess is wrong, the items are returned to the container.

7. The roles are reversed and play continues. Students take turns until the container is empty.
8. When the container is empty, students count the two sets of items. The student with more items is the winner.
9. If you wish, you could award a prize to each student for each subset of five items, plus an extra bonus for the winner. Another bonus could be given to any student who can state correctly whether his/her total is odd or even.

EXTENSIONS AND ADAPTATIONS
1. As students count their items, have them chart the numbers under the headings ODD and EVEN.
2. Vary the game by having two students reach into the container and grasp items. Have a third student guess whether the sum (or difference) is odd or even.
3. This activity is appropriate for use in a learning center.

ARITHMETIC MACHINE

PRIMARY CONTENT
Understanding number relationships and patterns

PRIOR STUDENT KNOWLEDGE
No special prior knowledge is required.

PRE-ACTIVITY PREPARATION
1. Construct an Arithmetic Machine as described on supplement Arithmetic Machine Plans (page 6).
2. Using unlined 3 in. x 5 in. index cards, make ten sets of function cards as exemplified on supplement Function Card Set Plans (page 7).
3. Copy reproducible Student Data Sheet (page 8), one to three copies per student. Each student will use one to three Student Data Sheets per session, depending on the number of function card sets used during the activity.

PROCESS SKILLS
Observing, comparing, calculating, recording, predicting, analyzing

GROUP SIZE
2 students
(It is recommended that this activity be used in a learning center rather than with the whole class.)

MATERIALS PER GROUP
- 1 Arithmetic Machine
- 10 function card sets
- 1–3 copies of reproducible Student Data Sheet for each student

TEACHER INFORMATION
After students have gone through the available sets of function cards a few times with the Arithmetic Machine, memory will replace analysis. Therefore, it is necessary to periodically develop new function card sets with new rules.

PROCEDURE

1. Student A takes a set of function cards and displays the IN face of the first card to student B. Student B records the IN value on the Student Data Sheet. Student A then puts the card, faceup, into the Arithmetic Machine. As the card comes out of the machine, student B observes the OUT face. Student B then records the OUT value on the Student Data Sheet.

2. Student A continues to display and place additional cards into the Arithmetic Machine until student B determines the rule and can predict the OUT value.

3. When student B thinks he/she knows the rule, student A allows student B to predict the OUT value of the next card after displaying the IN value. He/She then puts the card into the Arithmetic Machine and student B's prediction is checked as the card comes out.

4. For every correct prediction, student B gets one point—tallied in the Total Points Scored space on the Student Data Sheet. (Both the accuracy and speed of figuring out the rule is important in accumulating points, since there are only ten cards in each set.)

5. After the first set of cards is completed, students A and B reverse roles for the next set of cards.

6. Students who have the necessary skills should write the discovered rule for their card set in a word sentence. Younger students may describe the rule verbally.

7. A game consists of an equal number (one to five) of sets for both students. The student with the higher point total is the winner.

EXTENSIONS AND ADAPTATIONS

1. Have an Arithmetic Machine class tournament.

2. Challenge other classes to Arithmetic Machine tournaments, or let different classes choose individual "champions" to do battle.

3. Related activity In or Out on page 45.

ARITHMETIC MACHINE

ARITHMETIC MACHINE PLANS

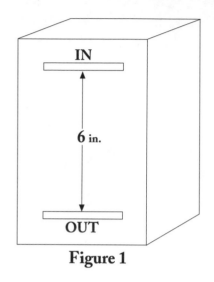

Figure 1

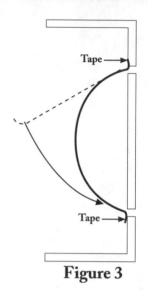

Figure 3

Materials:

- 1 cardboard box (shoebox or larg[e])
- 1 flexible sheet of cardboard
- masking tape
- 1 pair of scissors
- 1 utility knife
- decorating materials (paint, markers, etc.)

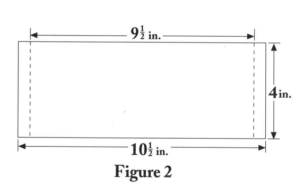

Figure 2

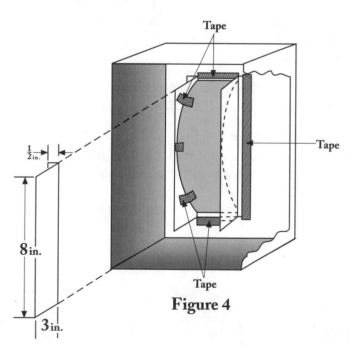

Figure 4

Directions:

Cut two 4 in. x $\frac{1}{2}$ in. slots as shown in Figure 1. Cut a flexible cardboard strip 4 in. x $10\frac{1}{2}$ in. as shown in Figure 2. Fold along the dotted lines. Tape one end of the flexible strip to the top edge of the IN slot as shown in Figure 3. Tape the other end to the bottom edge of the OUT slot. Close in both sides of the flexible strip by cutting cardboard and taping in place as shown in Figure 4. The outside of the box may be decorated to make it look like a "magic" box.

ARITHMETIC MACHINE

FUNCTION CARD SET PLANS

Card going into
Arithmetic Machine

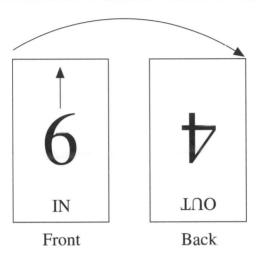

IN	OUT
6	4
Front	Back

Here are six sample sets. Each set contains ten cards.

Set 1		Set 2		Set 3		Set 4		Set 5		Set 6	
IN	OUT	IN	OUT	IN	OUT	IN	OUT	IN	OUT	IN	OUT
1	2	1	2	1	0	1	3	1	0	1	4
2	3	2	4	2	1	2	5	2	1	2	5
3	4	3	6	3	2	3	7	3	0	3	6
4	5	4	8	4	3	4	9	4	1	4	7
5	6	5	10	5	4	5	11	5	0	5	8
6	7	6	12	6	5	6	13	6	1	6	9
7	8	7	14	7	6	7	15	7	0	7	10
8	9	8	16	8	7	8	17	8	1	8	11
9	10	9	18	9	8	9	19	9	0	9	12
10	11	10	20	10	9	10	21	10	1	10	13
Rule or Function:	$n+1$		$2n$		$n-1$		$n+n+1$		n odd $= 0$ n even $= 1$		$n+3$

Construct four more sets using your own rules or functions.

ARITHMETIC MACHINE _____

STUDENT DATA SHEET

Name_____

DATA	
IN	OUT
___	___
___	___
___	___
___	___
___	___
___	___
___	___
___	___
___	___

Describe the IN-OUT rule or function for this set of cards.

_____

_____

_____

_____

_____

Total Points Scored: _____

DATA	
IN	OUT
___	___
___	___
___	___
___	___
___	___
___	___
___	___
___	___
___	___

Describe the IN-OUT rule or function for this set of cards.

_____

_____

_____

_____

_____

Total Points Scored: _____

FROM PLACE TO PLACE

PRIMARY CONTENT

Identifying the place value of each digit in a four-digit number

PRIOR STUDENT KNOWLEDGE

Number recognition and place value knowledge

PRE-ACTIVITY PREPARATION

Using 9 in. x 12 in. construction paper, make number cards. Make enough cards so that each student has one card. Write one number on each card. Use the number progression 0–9, repeating that progression or portion thereof until the correct number of cards are made. Shuffle the number cards so they are not in sequential order.

PROCESS SKILLS

Observing, classifying

GROUP SIZE

Whole class

MATERIALS PER GROUP

Number cards, 0–9, one number card per student

TEACHER INFORMATION

No special teacher information is required.

PROCEDURE

1. Randomly distribute the number cards, facedown, to the students. Students are not to reveal their numbers.

2. Select one student to be the Reader and have that student come to the front of the room without his/her number card. That student then chooses four classmates to come to the front of the room, bringing their number cards with them.

3. These four students stand shoulder-to-shoulder, facing the class and the Reader, in any left-to-right order they wish. They then display their number cards, forming a four-digit number.

4. The Reader must read the displayed number aloud and then identify the place value of each digit. For example, if the number 7,397 is displayed, the Reader should say "Seven thousand, three hundred, ninety-seven; 7 in the thousands place, 3 in the hundreds place, 9 in the tens place, and 7 in the ones place."

5. Assist the Reader if an error is made in reading the number and/or place value identification.

6. All five students return to their desks.

7. Repeat the procedure (steps 2–6) as many times as desired.

EXTENSIONS AND ADAPTATIONS

1. Fewer or more place values can be used according to the students' ability level.

2. Related activities The Bigger, the Better on page 10, Clowning Around on page 12, Toss 'Em on page 26, and Value the Place on page 34.

THE BIGGER, THE BETTER _____

PRIMARY CONTENT
- Comparing four-digit numbers, including usage of symbols <, >, =
- Identifying place value in four-digit numbers

PRIOR STUDENT KNOWLEDGE
Familiarity with place value of four-digit numbers

PRE-ACTIVITY PREPARATION
Using 9 in. x 12 in. construction paper, make two sets of number cards. Each set should consist of ten cards of the same color. (The colors of the two sets should be different.) On each card, write one number, 0–9.

PROCESS SKILLS
Observing, comparing, classifying, recording

GROUP SIZE
Whole class divided into two groups (teams)

MATERIALS PER GROUP
- 1 set of number cards

TEACHER INFORMATION

As written, The Bigger, the Better involves cooperative team activity as opposed to competitive activity. Thus, it needs to be stressed to students that the two teams are not racing against each other; nor is there a winner or a loser. However, if desired (and as indicated in the Extensions and Adaptations section), The Bigger, the Better could easily be adapted to a competitive activity.

10

PROCEDURE

1. Divide the class in half to make two teams. Put a set of number cards in front of each team. The card sets may be put in boxes set on desks; or they may be spread out on tables or the floor.

2. Each team identifies four students to go first, one to represent each place value: thousands, hundreds, tens, and ones.

3. Verbally give each team a different four-digit number. For example, you might give one team 4,683 and the other team 3,864.

4. Each of the four students identified to represent a place value selects the number card from the set for his/her place. At the front of the room, the four students hold up the cards to represent their team's number (formed so the class can read it in correct left-to-right progression). Team members may assist those who need help. You may want to write *thousands, hundreds, tens,* and *ones* on the chalkboard to assist students in standing in the correct place value.

5. For each four-digit number, discuss with students the place value of each digit and correct the lineup if necessary.

6. Now write the two numbers on the board side-by-side and ask students to indicate whether a <, >, or = symbol should be used between the numbers to make a true statement.

7. Each team then selects the next four students to represent the place values, and the process is repeated.

8. Continue until each student has had at least one opportunity to represent a place value.

EXTENSIONS AND ADAPTATIONS

1. Develop rules to make the activity into a competitive game.

2. Related activities From Place to Place on page 9, Clowning Around on page 12, Compare and Capture on page 14, Toss 'Em on page 26, and Value the Place on page 34.

CLOWNING AROUND _____

PRIMARY CONTENT

Identifying place value in four-digit numbers

PRIOR STUDENT KNOWLEDGE

Familiarity with place value

PRE-ACTIVITY PREPARATION

The Clowning Around playing board is a large grid with numbers ranging from one digit to four digits. On two large sheets of poster board, construct two playing boards using the supplement Playing-Board Grid on page 13 as a guide. To make a clown face appear, add color to the playing boards as follows: color all the squares with one-digit numbers yellow, those with two-digit numbers orange, those with three-digit numbers red; leave those with four-digit numbers white.

PROCESS SKILLS

Observing, classifying

GROUP SIZE

Whole class divided into four groups (teams)

MATERIALS PER GROUP

- 2 playing boards for whole class (1 playing board per 2 groups)
- 2 bean bags for whole class (1 bean bag per 2 groups)

TEACHER INFORMATION

No special teacher information is required.

PROCEDURE

1. Push desks to the periphery of the room to make a play area. Place the playing boards and bean bags on the floor at opposite ends of the room.

2. Divide the class into four teams. Each team selects one student to act as their scorekeeper. (The scorekeeper still plays in the game.)

3. There will be two teams at each playing board and the teams take turns.

4. Have students stand about two feet away from the playing board. Have one student throw the bean bag onto the playing board.

5. The student must then tell what place value each digit is in. (For example, if the bean bag landed on 82, the student must say that 8 is in the tens place

and 2 is in the ones place.) If the bean bag lands on more than one square, the student may choose which number to play. If the bean bag misses the playing board, the student may throw again.

6. The student's team gets one point for each digit whose place value was correctly stated.

7. Play continues until all students have taken a turn.

8. The winning team is the one with the most points.

EXTENSIONS AND ADAPTATIONS

1. To use as a small-group activity, make smaller playing boards and have students toss coins onto the boards.

2. For younger students, practice identifying place value in one-digit numbers and two-digit numbers.

3. Related activities From Place to Place on page 9, The Bigger, the Better on page 10, Toss 'Em on page 26, and Value the Place on page 34.

CLOWNING AROUND _____

PLAYING-BOARD GRID

Name _____

6	9	5	4	6	7	9	4	3	2	1	0
3	121	142	236	4	5	9	6	361	497	142	2
394	697	142	397	2,931	4,962	5,931	4,987	241	794	131	212
415	693	412	4,912	6,291	1,987	6,543	2,142	1,666	493	646	794
2	216	111	7,932	23	6,321	4,931	41	7,892	133	499	2
1	7	9	4,444	1,232	962	984	4,968	4,221	8	4	3
3	4	8	9,321	2,146	489	132	6,784	1,234	9	7	1
6	9	3	1,239	6,421	1,122	3,314	4,932	1,423	0	4	1
4	6	8	9	2,351	1,567	1,423	6,987	8	6	5	2
3	5	7	52	49	1,212	3,461	76	84	7	4	3
2	1	31	82	79	51	44	39	68	91	5	8
0	1	2	18	24	3	4	76	92	7	6	9
2	3	4	9	7	5	1	3	2	4	6	7

Mathematics Activities (KSAM)

COMPARE AND CAPTURE _____

PRIMARY CONTENT
- Determining which number amount is larger, smaller, or equal to another
- Using the symbols >, <, and =
- Adding and subtracting one-digit numbers
- Solving open number sentences

PRIOR STUDENT KNOWLEDGE
Basic one-digit addition and subtraction facts; previous exposure to the symbols >, <, and =

PRE-ACTIVITY PREPARATION
1. By cutting 3 in. x 5 in. index cards in half, prepare a set of twenty-four $1\frac{1}{2}$ in. x 5 in. number-sentence strips (tongue depressors may be substituted if available). On one side of each strip, write one of the twenty-four open number sentences listed in step 1 of the Procedure. (Note that the number sentences listed represent only twenty-four examples. There are many other possible examples.) Prepare one set for each group.
2. Use two blank cubes to prepare a set of cubes for each group. On the faces of one cube, write the numbers 0, 1, 2, 3, 8, and 9. On the faces of the second cube, write the numbers 1, 3, 4, 5, 6, and 7. (Blank cubes of various sizes and compositions can be found at most hobby shops, craft stores, and teacher supply stores.)

PROCESS SKILLS
Observing, comparing, calculating

GROUP SIZE
2 students

MATERIALS PER GROUP
- 24 number-sentence strips
- 2 cubes

TEACHER INFORMATION
No special teacher information is required.

PROCEDURE

1. Distribute the cubes and number-sentence strips (facedown) to each group. The strips will be marked with the following twenty-four open number sentences:

☐ – ☐ = 0	☐ + ☐ = 8	☐ + ☐ < 16
☐ + ☐ > 1	☐ – ☐ < 9	☐ + ☐ < 17
☐ – ☐ > 2	☐ + ☐ < 10	☐ – ☐ < 18
☐ + ☐ > 3	☐ + ☐ > 11	☐ – 2 < ☐
☐ – ☐ = 4	☐ + ☐ = 12	☐ – 3 < ☐
☐ – ☐ < 5	☐ – ☐ < 13	☐ + 4 < ☐
☐ + ☐ = 6	☐ + ☐ > 14	☐ + 5 < ☐
☐ + ☐ > 7	☐ – ☐ < 15	☐ + 5 > ☐

2. Each player takes twelve strips and arranges them faceup.

3. Order of play is determined by the throw of the same die (cube). The player with the highest number goes first.

4. The first player rolls both dice. If the two numbers rolled complete a true sentence for any one of that player's strips, that strip is removed from the playing field and set aside. Only one strip may be removed per roll, and only one roll is allowed per turn.

5. The second player takes a turn, repeating step 4.

6. If a player makes an error (for example, removes a strip that did not make a true statement with the numbers rolled), the strip is returned to the playing field and the player loses a turn. (Players check each other's accuracy.)

7. Play continues until one player's strips are all set aside.

EXTENSIONS AND ADAPTATIONS

1. Groups of three students can play, but each student will select eight number-sentence strips. Likewise, groups of four students can play, each selecting six number-sentence strips.

2. This is also an appropriate activity for pair or small-group use in a learning center. Such use requires the preparation of only one or two sets of number-sentence strips and dice.

3. Related activities The Bigger, the Better on page 10 and The Unknown Number on page 30 (for number comparison and use of the symbols >, <, and =).

4 Related activities Bad Call on page 46 and Pick As Many As You Can on page 60 (for basic addition and subtraction facts).

A FRACTION OF AN EGG

PRIMARY CONTENT
- Comparing fractions with a numerator of 1
- Using less than or greater than

PRIOR STUDENT KNOWLEDGE

Previous exposure to fractions and familiarity with the terms *numerator* and *denominator*

PRE-ACTIVITY PREPARATION

1. Using 3 in. x 5 in. index cards, make one set of fraction cards for each group. Each set should contain five cards, with a different fraction displayed on each card. The fractions to be used are $\frac{1}{2}$, $\frac{1}{3}$, $\frac{1}{4}$, $\frac{1}{6}$, and $\frac{1}{12}$.
2. Copy reproducibles Fraction Sheet 1 (page 18) and Fraction Sheet 2 (page 19), one copy of each per student.

PROCESS SKILLS

Observing, comparing, recording

GROUP SIZE

5 students

MATERIALS PER GROUP
- 5 egg cartons (12-egg size)
- At least 16 marbles
- 1 paper cup to hold marbles
- 1 set of fraction cards
- 1 copy of reproducible Fraction Sheet 1 for each student
- 1 copy of reproducible Fraction Sheet 2 for each student

TEACHER INFORMATION

Unlike with a whole number, as the denominator of a fraction increases, the size of the fraction decreases. This is a difficult concept for many students to fully grasp because it appears to them to be contrary to what they have previously learned about whole numbers. This activity helps put this concept into a more observable, concrete form.

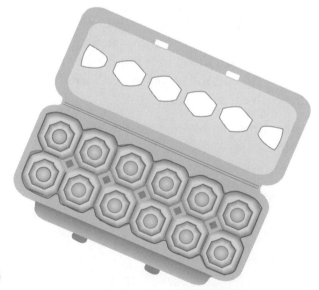

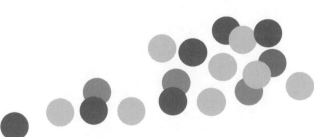

PROCEDURE

1. Divide students into groups of five. Distribute to each group all the materials except the reproducibles. (If class does not divide evenly into groups of five, any smaller size group will do; each group, however, still needs 5 egg cartons and at least 16 marbles.)

2. Each student receives an egg carton with which to work. (In smaller groups, some students will have two or more egg cartons.)

3. Have the first student in each group put one marble in each space of his/her egg carton until $\frac{1}{2}$ of the carton is filled. Other students in the group may help if needed. Then have students place by that carton the fraction card displaying $\frac{1}{2}$.

4. Have the second student in each group put one marble in each space of his/her egg carton until $\frac{1}{3}$ of the carton is filled. Other students in the group may help if needed. Then have students place by that carton the fraction card displaying $\frac{1}{3}$. (Students should keep the marbles in each carton as they complete the activity.)

5. Continue as in steps 3 and 4, with the third student making $\frac{1}{4}$, the fourth student making $\frac{1}{6}$, and the fifth student making $\frac{1}{12}$.

6. Distribute reproducible Fraction Sheet 1 to each student. Have students fill in the table, using the marbles that are in the egg cartons as a reference. (See Answer Key, page 152.)

7. Encourage each group to discuss, among themselves, the three questions below the table on Fraction Sheet 1 and attempt to reach group-based conclusions. Each student in the group should then write those conclusions in the appropriate spaces. (See Answer Key, page 152.)

8. Let students from different groups share their findings. Use findings as the base for a class discussion/summary, including questions such as:
   - Would $\frac{1}{3}$ be less than or greater than $\frac{1}{6}$?
   - Would $\frac{1}{2}$ be less than or greater than $\frac{1}{4}$?
   - Would $\frac{1}{4}$ be less than or greater than $\frac{1}{12}$?
   - Would $\frac{1}{12}$ be less than or greater than $\frac{1}{6}$?
   - Would $\frac{1}{3}$ be less than or greater than $\frac{1}{2}$?

9. Distribute reproducible Fraction Sheet 2 to each student for individual practice and evaluation. (See Answer Key, page 152.)

EXTENSIONS AND ADAPTATIONS

1. Have students convert the fractions to a common denominator (12). Fractions could then be added to get a sum.

2. For students with the appropriate background, money (the dollar and fractional parts of the dollar)—$\frac{1}{2}$ or half dollar, $\frac{1}{4}$ or quarter, $\frac{1}{10}$ or dime, $\frac{1}{20}$ or nickel, $\frac{1}{100}$ or penny—clearly illustrates the concept that as the denominator increases, the size of the fraction (the amount it represents) decreases.

3. Related activity Mom and Apple Pie on page 40.

A FRACTION OF AN EGG

FRACTION SHEET 1

Name_____

1. Complete the table. Write the number of spaces used to make the fractions.

Fraction	Spaces Used
$\frac{1}{12}$	
$\frac{1}{6}$	
$\frac{1}{4}$	
$\frac{1}{3}$	
$\frac{1}{2}$	

2. What do you notice about the numerators of the fractions?

_____

_____

_____

3. Now look at the denominators and the number of spaces used. What happens to the denominators compared to what happens to the number of spaces used?

_____

_____

_____

4. Look at the egg cartons. What happens to the fraction as the denominator gets larger?

_____

_____

_____

A FRACTION OF AN EGG _____

FRACTION SHEET 2

Name_____

Directions: For each item, look at the two fractions. Decide if the first fraction is less than or greater than the second fraction. Circle the correct answer (less than or greater than). Look at the example.

Example:

$\frac{1}{2}$ is less than / (greater than) $\frac{1}{3}$.

1. $\frac{1}{7}$ is less than / greater than $\frac{1}{4}$.

2. $\frac{1}{6}$ is less than / greater than $\frac{1}{9}$.

3. $\frac{1}{3}$ is less than / greater than $\frac{1}{20}$.

4. $\frac{1}{11}$ is less than / greater than $\frac{1}{34}$.

5. $\frac{1}{14}$ is less than / greater than $\frac{1}{10}$.

6. $\frac{1}{10}$ is less than / greater than $\frac{1}{4}$.

7. $\frac{1}{12}$ is less than / greater than $\frac{1}{26}$.

8. $\frac{1}{17}$ is less than / greater than $\frac{1}{22}$.

9. $\frac{1}{8}$ is less than / greater than $\frac{1}{3}$.

10. $\frac{1}{14}$ is less than / greater than $\frac{1}{6}$.

SKIP TO MY LOU _____

PRIMARY CONTENT

Patterning by skip counting

PRIOR STUDENT KNOWLEDGE

Counting by ones; some previous exposure to the use of a calculator

PRE-ACTIVITY PREPARATION

1. Copy reproducible Hundreds Chart 1 (page 23), several copies (at least five) for each student. The number of copies per student depends on the number of skip-patterns you want students to see.
2. (Optional) Make an overhead transparency using the reproducible supplement Calculator Transparency (page 22).

PROCESS SKILLS

Observing, comparing, classifying, counting, estimating, recording

GROUP SIZE

Individual or pairs

MATERIALS PER GROUP

- 1 four-function calculator
- (Optional) Overhead projector (for whole class)
- (Optional) Calculator Transparency (for whole class)
- Paper and pencil
- 1 stop watch (or room clock with second hand for whole class)
- 1 light-colored crayon for each student
- 5 or more copies of reproducible Hundreds Chart 1 for each student

TEACHER INFORMATION

For this activity, you should be thoroughly familiar with the use of a constant for addition or subtraction. Each calculator has instructions on how to do this. Most calculators use the same method, yet there may be differences. (See step 10 in Procedure.) Also, not all calculator keys will be labeled the same. (For example, AC on some calculators may be C on others or CE—hit twice—on still others.) Thus, it is critical that you are competent in the use of the calculator employed in the classroom.

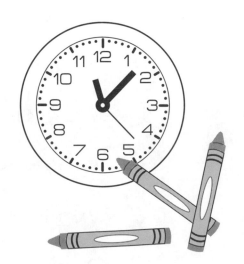

PROCEDURE

1. Pass out calculators and allow a few minutes for exploration.

2. Teach (or review) the use of the number keys; +, -, x, ÷, and =; and how to enter a constant for addition and skip counting. (Optional: use the Calculator Transparency and overhead to aid this instruction.)

3. Tell students to estimate the number of seconds it will take them to count to 50 using skip counting by 1s on the calculator. Have students each record the estimate on a separate sheet of paper.

4. Have students perform these key strokes.

   a. Press the AC (All Clear) key.

   b. Press the 1 key.

   c. Press the + key twice.

   d. TAKE YOUR HANDS OFF THE CALCULATOR.

5. Now have students start on your signal and time how long it takes them to count to 50 (by 1s) on their calculators by pressing the = key repeatedly. Students should raise their hands when finished, and then they should compare their actual times with their estimates.

6. Have students try the following in the same manner:

   a. Count to 100 by 1s.

   b. Count to 100 by 2s.

   c. Count to 99 by 3s.

   d. Count to 100 by 4s.

   e. Count to 100 by 5s.

   f. Make up your own activities.

7. Distribute a crayon and at least five copies of Hundreds Chart 1 to each student.

8. Tell students to use the calculators to count to 100 by 2s and to color the numbers in the count on their number charts as they proceed. Once they discover the pattern, let them color the rest of the numbers without the calculator.

9. Have students use a clean chart for each count and perform the same activity as in step 8 using skip counting by 3s, 4s, 5s, etc., coloring in numbers as they count.

10. Direct students to enter 10 as the constant added. Have students enter 3 as the first number and then skip count, 3, 13, 23, 33, 43, 53. . . Have students color in these numbers on the number chart and note the patterns.
(Key strokes: AC, 10 + 3 =) (Note that with some calculators, the procedure is reversed—i.e., AC, 3 + 10 =.)

EXTENSIONS AND ADAPTATIONS

1. Have students predict elapsed time for counting to 100 after they know their time to 50. Also have them predict time for counting by 2s or 3s to 100, etc.

2. Have students use a hundreds chart with only seven numbers in each row. (See reproducible Hundreds Chart 2 on page 25.) Note the pattern formed when the numbers are colored in during counts by 2s or 3s.

3. This activity is appropriate for individual or small group use in a learning center.

SKIP TO MY LOU

CALCULATOR TRANSPARENCY

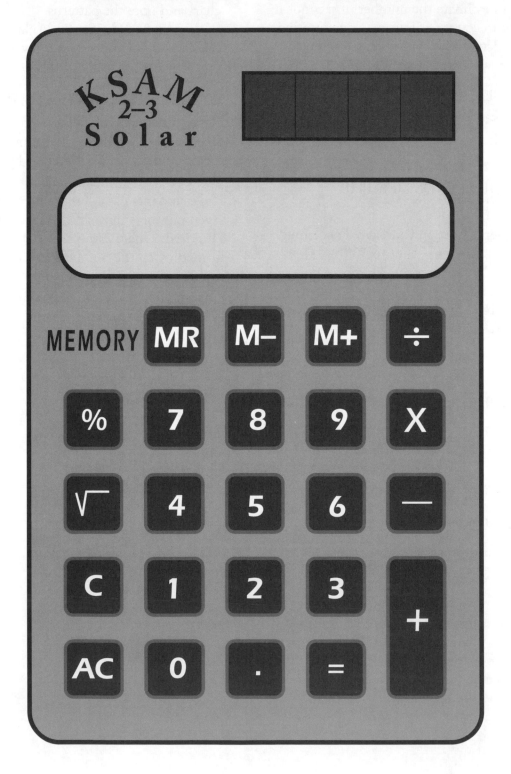

SKIP TO MY LOU

HUNDREDS CHART 1

Name

1	2	3	4	5	6	7	8	9	10
11	12	13	14	15	16	17	18	19	20
21	22	23	24	25	26	27	28	29	30
31	32	33	34	35	36	37	38	39	40
41	42	43	44	45	46	47	48	49	50
51	52	53	54	55	56	57	58	59	60
61	62	63	64	65	66	67	68	69	70
71	72	73	74	75	76	77	78	79	80
81	82	83	84	85	86	87	88	89	90
91	92	93	94	95	96	97	98	99	100

SKIP TO MY LOU ⎯⎯⎯⎯⎯⎯⎯⎯⎯⎯⎯⎯

HUNDREDS CHART 2

Name⎯⎯⎯⎯⎯⎯⎯⎯⎯⎯⎯⎯⎯⎯⎯⎯⎯⎯⎯⎯⎯⎯

1	2	3	4	5	6	7
8	9	10	11	12	13	14
15	16	17	18	19	20	21
22	23	24	25	26	27	28
29	30	31	32	33	34	35
36	37	38	39	40	41	42
43	44	45	46	47	48	49
50	51	52	53	54	55	56
57	58	59	60	61	62	63
64	65	66	67	68	69	70
71	72	73	74	75	76	77
78	79	80	81	82	83	84
85	86	87	88	89	90	91
92	93	94	95	96	97	98
99	100	101	102	103	104	105

ACTIVITY
9

TOSS 'EM

PRIMARY CONTENT

Identifying the place value of each digit in a number having four (or fewer) digits

PRIOR STUDENT KNOWLEDGE

Knowledge that 10 ones = 1 ten,
10 tens = 1 hundred,
10 hundreds = 1 thousand

PRE-ACTIVITY PREPARATION

1. Prepare a Toss 'Em materials set for small-group use in a learning center. A set consists of nine toothpicks or "beheaded" kitchen matches (to represent ones), nine popsicle sticks (to represent tens), nine unsharpened pencils, tongue depressors, or 8 in. long dowel rods (to represent hundreds), and nine 12 in. wooden rulers or 12 in. long dowel rods (to represent thousands). Put the materials in an open box with the value of each item clearly displayed on the outside of the box. (For example, toothpick = 1, popsicle stick = 10, pencil = 100, ruler = 1,000).

2. Copy reproducible Student Data Sheet (page 29), enough for an adequate supply at the learning center. (Each student will use one Student Data Sheet per session.)

PROCESS SKILLS

Observing, classifying, sorting, counting, recording, inferring

GROUP SIZE

2 students
(It is recommended that this activity be used in a learning center rather than with the whole class.)

MATERIALS PER GROUP

• 1 Toss 'Em materials set
• 1 copy of reproducible Student Data Sheet for each student

TEACHER INFORMATION

No special teacher information is required.

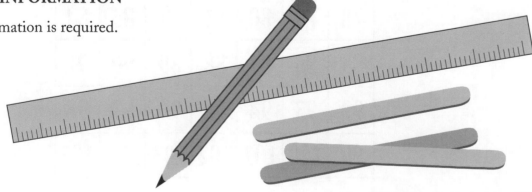

PROCEDURE

1. One student is the Tosser. That student reaches into the Toss 'Em box and withdraws any mix of the various items. (It is not required that items representing every place value be included.) The items are then tossed onto the table.

2. The second student is the Writer. That student groups the items according to place value in proper left-to-right progression, recording (numerically or with tally marks) on the Student Data Sheet the number of items in each grouping. The complete number should then be written in the appropriate space on the Student Data Sheet. Any one-digit to four-digit number is a possibility.

3. If both students agree that the grouping and written number are correct, a point is awarded to the Writer. If there is a disagreement, the students consult with the teacher.

4. Students then switch roles, and steps 1–3 are repeated. After a few tosses, students will begin to develop various tossing strategies in an attempt to foil their opponents.

5. Students continue to take turns throughout the activity. A complete game can either be defined by time (for example, ten minutes) or by the number of tosses (for example, twelve tosses for each student). The student with more points at the end of the game is the winner. Ties are allowed.

EXTENSIONS AND ADAPTATIONS

1. Instead of the indicated materials, toothpicks can be bundled (with bundles taped or with both ends of a bundle dipped in glue) and used to show actual number of units. For example,
   1 = 1 toothpick
   10 = 1 bundle of 10 toothpicks
   100 = 10 bundles of 10 toothpicks
   1,000 = 100 bundles of 10 toothpicks

2. Related activities From Place to Place on page 9, The Bigger, the Better on page 10, Clowning Around on page 12, and Value the Place on page 34.

TOSS 'EM _____

STUDENT DATA SHEET

Name_____

1. _____
   1,000s   100s   10s   1s   NUMBER   POINT

2. _____
   1,000s   100s   10s   1s   NUMBER   POINT

3. _____
   1,000s   100s   10s   1s   NUMBER   POINT

4. _____
   1,000s   100s   10s   1s   NUMBER   POINT

5. _____
   1,000s   100s   10s   1s   NUMBER   POINT

6. _____
   1,000s   100s   10s   1s   NUMBER   POINT

7. _____
   1,000s   100s   10s   1s   NUMBER   POINT

8. _____
   1,000s   100s   10s   1s   NUMBER   POINT

9. _____
   1,000s   100s   10s   1s   NUMBER   POINT

10. _____
   1,000s   100s   10s   1s   NUMBER   POINT

11. _____
   1,000s   100s   10s   1s   NUMBER   POINT

12. _____
   1,000s   100s   10s   1s   NUMBER   POINT

TOTAL POINTS _____

THE UNKNOWN NUMBER _____

PRIMARY CONTENT
Comparing two-digit numbers, using the symbols < and >

PRIOR STUDENT KNOWLEDGE
Familiarity with the symbols < and > (meaning "less than" and "greater than")

PRE-ACTIVITY PREPARATION
Cut at least six 3 in. x 6 in. strips of construction paper. On each strip, write a number selected at random between 0-100. One strip is required for each time the game is played. If it is desired that the game be played more than six times, cut additional strips.

PROCESS SKILLS
Observing, comparing, recording, analyzing, interpreting

GROUP SIZE
Whole class

MATERIALS PER GROUP
- 1 safety pin
- 6 prepared number strips

TEACHER INFORMATION

Trying to determine an unknown number through less-than, greater-than guessing is a lot of fun for students. However, some guessing strategies are much more effective than others. This game provides a good opportunity for you to aid students in developing good guessing strategies.

PROCEDURE

1. Draw large < and > symbols on the board.

2. Select one student to come to the front of the room.

3. Pin a number strip on the student's back without the student knowing what the number is.

4. Have the student turn around, allowing the rest of the class to see the number. Tell the class to write the number on a piece of paper so they won't forget it.

5. The student then makes a guess at any number between 0 and 100 and asks a student in the class if his/her guess is less than or greater than the number on the strip (unknown to the student).

6. The guess is then recorded on the board under < if the guess is less than the unknown number. The guess is recorded under > if it is greater than the unknown number.

7. The student then makes another guess and asks another student if it is greater than or less than the unknown number.

8. The guess is again recorded under the correct sign.

9. Guessing and recording continues until the unknown number is discovered.

10. Repeat the game with a new student and a new number strip. At least six rounds are recommended.

EXTENSIONS AND ADAPTATIONS

1. This activity lends itself well to competitive games among individual students or teams.

2. Use numbers between 100-999 on the number strips.

3. Use all odd numbers or all even numbers on the number strips.

4. Pin a number on the back of every student. Students can then roam around the room or interact at other appropriate times during the day, asking each other if their guess is greater than or less than their unknown number. Responses are recorded on the reproducible Student Data Sheet, page 33.

5. Related activities The Bigger, the Better on page 10 and Compare and Capture on page 14.

THE UNKNOWN NUMBER

STUDENT DATA SHEET

Name_____

My unknown number is _____ .

STUDENT ASKED	> GREATER THAN	< LESS THAN

VALUE THE PLACE _____

PRIMARY CONTENT
Identifying place value in three-digit numbers

PRIOR STUDENT KNOWLEDGE
Basic understanding of place value

PRE-ACTIVITY PREPARATION

1. Make three sets of number cards on 9 in. x 12 in. construction paper, with the color of the paper being the same within sets but different between sets. Each set should consist of as many cards as the number of students in a group. (For example, a class of twenty-six students yields three student groups of eight which results in three sets of number cards, each set consisting of eight cards.) Each number card in a set displays a different number, beginning with 0 and extending upward consecutively until all cards have been numbered. (In the example above with groups of eight, each set would contain the numbers 0–7.)

2. Use 9 in. x 12 in. construction paper to make a ONES sign, a TENS sign, and a HUNDREDS sign for each set in the set's color.

3. On 3 in. x 5 in. cards, make twenty-five to fifty flashcards of three-digit numbers, using all the numbers for which number cards were made in step 1. (If desired, two-digit numbers and one-digit numbers could be included as well.) Do not use a number more than once on the same card.

PROCESS SKILLS
Observing, classifying

GROUP SIZE
Whole class divided into 3 equal groups (teams)

MATERIALS PER GROUP
- 1 set of number cards
- 1 set of number signs
- 1 set of flashcards (for whole class)

TEACHER INFORMATION
No special teacher information is required.

PROCEDURE

1. Distribute a set of number cards to each team, with each team member being responsible for one of the numbers.

2. Other tasks are assigned as follows: If there are no extra students (for example, the class divides evenly into three groups), the teacher is the Caller, the Scorekeeper, and the Checker. If there are extra students (the number of students in the class does not divide evenly into three groups), extra students take over the roles of Scorekeeper and Caller.

3. On the board, tape the ONES, TENS, and HUNDREDS signs a distance from each other as shown below.

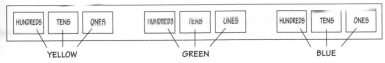

4. Using the flashcards, the Caller calls out a number (527, 103, 620, etc.).

5. The students in each team holding the corresponding digits each stand in front of the correct sign on the board to make the number.

6. The team that correctly makes its number first wins one point.

7. As play continues, rotate the Caller and Scorekeeper, (if any).

8. The team with the most points at the end of the game is the winning team.

EXTENSIONS AND ADAPTATIONS

1. Use the same procedure with the thousands place, ten-thousands place, etc.

2. Call out addition or subtraction problems (in place of numbers), and have students make their answers with their number cards. Make sure none of the answers contain any number more than once.

3. Related activities From Place to Place on page 9, The Bigger, the Better on page 10, Clowning Around on page 12, and Toss 'Em on page 26.

WHO'S ON FIRST?

PRIMARY CONTENT
- Ordinal number names, first through twenty-fifth
- Working with ordinal numbers

PRIOR STUDENT KNOWLEDGE
Ability to count and sequence, 1–24

PRE-ACTIVITY PREPARATION
Copy reproducibles Willy Worm (page 38) and Willy's Parts (page 39), one copy of each per student.

PROCESS SKILLS
Observing, comparing, classifying, counting

GROUP SIZE
Individual

MATERIALS PER GROUP
- 1 copy of reproducible Willy Worm
- 1 copy of reproducible Willy's Parts
- Scissors
- Glue
- Crayons

TEACHER INFORMATION
No special teacher information is required.

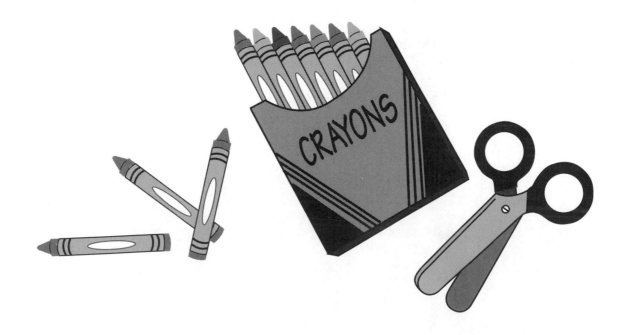

PROCEDURE

1. Review with students the difference between cardinal numbers and ordinal numbers. Make sure students understand that cardinal numbers imply a quantity, while ordinal numbers indicate an order or progression. Give a few examples of how ordinal numbers are commonly used (naming grades in school, innings in a ball game, quarters in a basketball game, etc.). Go over the ordinal number names, first through twenty-fourth, writing each name on the board.

2. Distribute materials to each student.

3. Draw students' attention to the reproducible Willy Worm. Tell them that this caterpillar's name is Willy Worm and that he is a very absent-minded caterpillar. In fact, he has misplaced several of his parts or segments, and just as bad, Willy has also lost his color. It is up to each student to get Willy back in shape by getting his parts and his color back to him.

4. Now direct students to the reproducible Willy's Parts. Instruct the students as described in steps 5–8.

5. Separate the top half from the bottom half of the page by cutting along the solid line.

6. The top half contains the eight parts that Willy has lost, and each part is labeled as to where it belongs in Willy's body. Cut out each part and then glue each part back into Willy at the right location in his body. (Willy's head is his first part.)

7. Don't forget to draw some legs onto the missing parts after you have glued them back into Willy's body.

8. When you have finished gluing the parts, take the bottom half of the page and closely follow the directions to give Willy back his color. (Help individual students with reading if necessary.) You may also color the rest of the page if desired.

9. When students have finished with Willy, collect and check drawings for ordinal correctness.

10. Display student pictures of Willy in the room or hallway.

EXTENSIONS AND ADAPTATIONS

1. Verbally assign an ordinal number to each student or give each student a hang sign with an ordinal number written on it. (Use the ordinal number *first* through the total number of students in the class.) All day students must line up (at breaks, recesses, lunch, etc.) according to their ordinal positions.

2. Challenge students to think of as many ways/situations as possible in which ordinal numbers are commonly used.

WHO'S ON FIRST? _____

WILLY WORM

Name_____

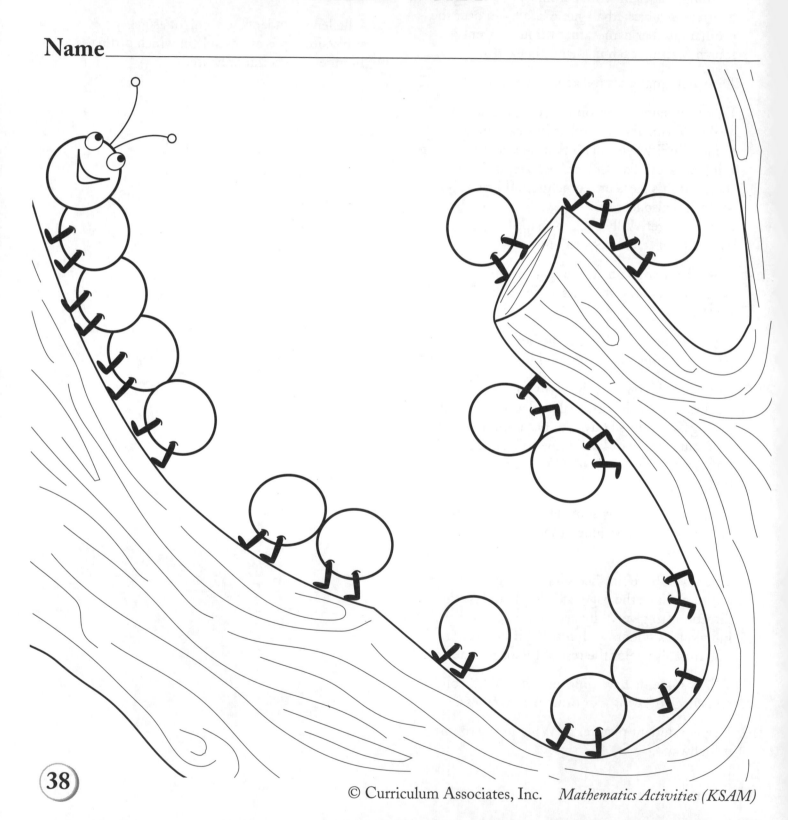

WHO'S ON FIRST?

WILLY'S PARTS

Name

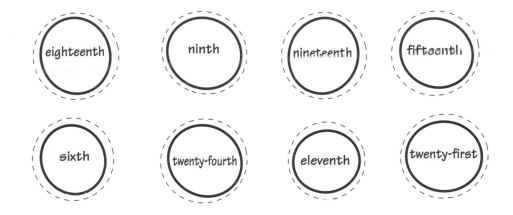

**DON'T FORGET TO GIVE THESE PARTS SOME LEGS
AFTER YOU GET THEM BACK INTO WILLY!**

AFTER YOU HAVE GLUED WILLY'S MISSING PARTS BACK ON,
FOLLOW THE DIRECTIONS BELOW TO GIVE WILLY SOME COLOR.

Color the **seventeenth** part of Willy **red**.

Color the **sixth** part of Willy **blue**.

Color the **twenty-third** part of Willy **black**.

Color the **eleventh** part of Willy **yellow**.

Color the **thirteenth** part of Willy **pink**.

Color the **second** part of Willy **orange**.

Color the **twenty-fourth** part of Willy **purple**.

Color the **twentieth** part of Willy **brown**.

Color all the **other** parts of Willy **green**.

MOM AND APPLE PIE

PRIMARY CONTENT

Recognizing fractional parts (thirds, fourths, sixths, and eighths)

PRIOR STUDENT KNOWLEDGE

Concept of fractional parts (thirds, fourths, sixths, and eighths)

PRE-ACTIVITY PREPARATION

Copy reproducible Hot Apple Pie (page 42), four copies per student.

PROCESS SKILLS

Observing, comparing, classifying

GROUP SIZE

Individual

MATERIALS PER GROUP

- Crayons
- 1 straightedge
- 4 copies of reproducible Hot Apple Pie

TEACHER INFORMATION

No special teacher information is required.

PROCEDURE

1. Introduce the activity by asking how many students have ever eaten freshly baked apple pie. Ask if they have ever seen anyone eat apple pie with toppings on it and, if so, what kind of toppings. Write the various toppings on the board. (The most common are ice cream, raisins, cheese, sugar, whipped cream, and cinnamon.) Tell students that today they are going to be serving slices of imaginary apple pies to their friends.

2. Distribute materials to each student.

3. Give students the following setup: "Your Mom has just baked a fresh, delicious apple pie. You bring two friends home with you after school. The three of you see the pie on the kitchen table and decide to eat the whole pie. To be fair, everyone should get an equal-sized piece. You are the only one who thinks you can cut the pie into three equal-sized, wedge-shaped pieces. Let's see if you really can."

4. Give students directions as outlined in steps 5–7.

5. Take one of your Hot Apple Pie sheets and color the pie as you wish. If you want, you may also add on, and color, any topping or combinations of toppings.

6. When you have finished coloring, use your straightedge and black crayon to divide the pie into three equal-sized, wedge-shaped pieces. Also answer the four questions at the bottom of your pie sheet. Raise your hand when you are done.

7. As students finish, check their pies to see if the pieces adequately represent the concept of thirds.

8. Repeat steps 3–7 for a pie to be divided into four pieces, then again for a six-piece pie, and finally for an eight-piece pie. During the students' work, give assistance as needed by showing that an eight-piece pie can be obtained by equally dividing a four-piece pie; and that sixths can be obtained by equally dividing thirds.

9. Review results with students, going over the correct procedure for obtaining the various pie pieces.

EXTENSIONS AND ADAPTATIONS

1. A similar activity can be done using other fractional parts.

2. This activity is suitable for use in a learning center.

3. Related activity A Fraction of an Egg on page 16.

MOM AND APPLE PIE _____

HOT APPLE PIE

Name_____

1. How many people are to be served this pie? _____

2. Into how many pieces did you cut this pie? _____

3. Are the pieces all the same size? _____

4. One piece equals what fraction of this whole pie? _____

Mathematics Activities (KSAM)

COMPUTATION AND BASIC SKILLS

IN OR OUT

PRIMARY CONTENT

Problem solving with fundamental
mathematical operations

PROCESS SKILLS

Comparing, classifying, inferring, predicting,
analyzing, problem solving

PRIOR STUDENT KNOWLEDGE

Experience in fundamental math operations

GROUP SIZE

Whole class

PRE-ACTIVITY PREPARATION

No special pre-activity preparation is required.

MATERIALS PER GROUP

No special materials are required.

TEACHER INFORMATION

No special teacher information is required.

PROCEDURE

1. Draw a large circle on the board.

2. Think of a rule to describe a set of numbers but
don't reveal the rule to students. (See examples of
rules that follow.) In the circle, write two or three
sample numbers that conform to the rule.

   Suggested Rules:
   odd numbers
   even numbers
   numbers more than 21
   numbers less than 37
   numbers with two digits
   numbers with double digits (11, 22, etc.)
   multiples of 3
   numbers with first digit larger than second
   even numbers less than 26
   multiples of 3

3. Select a student to pick a number (usually in a given
range, such as 1–50, depending on the grade level).
Write the number inside the circle if it is in the set
(fits the rule). Write the number outside the circle if

it is not in the set (does not conform to the rule). An
example is shown below for the rule "multiples of 3."

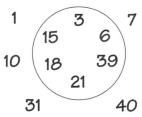

4. Students continue to pick numbers, which you
write inside or outside of the circle. Continue until
a student indicates that he/she knows the rule. Test
by asking that student to correctly place one or two
numbers that you choose.

5. Choose another rule and play again, or you may
let the winning student make up a rule and run
the game as before.

EXTENSIONS AND ADAPTATIONS

1. Play the game using a larger set of numbers, such
as 1–100.

2. Make up and use rules in addition to those
suggested. (For example, numbers greater than 20
and less than 40.)

3. Related activity Arithmetic Machine on page 4.

BAD CALL

PRIMARY CONTENT

Computing answers using addition, subtraction, and multiplication of whole numbers

PRIOR STUDENT KNOWLEDGE

Familiarity with addition, subtraction, and multiplication

PRE-ACTIVITY PREPARATION

1. Copy reproducible Umpire (page 48), one copy per student.
2. Depending on the operation(s) for which practice is desired, copy one or more of the following reproducibles for each student: Addition Problems (page 49), Subtraction Problems (page 50), and Multiplication Problems (page 51).

PROCESS SKILLS

Observing, comparing, calculating

GROUP SIZE

Individual

MATERIALS PER GROUP

- 1 copy of reproducible Umpire
- 1 copy of reproducible Addition Problems
- 1 copy of reproducible Subtraction Problems
- 1 copy of reproducible Multiplication Problems

TEACHER INFORMATION

Bad Call combines a hidden number game with the basic operations of addition, subtraction, and multiplication of whole numbers. The activity is designed, and the reproducibles are constructed, so that one, two, or all three operations can be addressed. The locations of the hidden numbers are as follows:

nose = 0	mouth = 5
right shoulder = 1	elbow = 6
left arm = 2	left shoulder = 7
fingers = 3	eyes = 8
hat = 4	ear = 9

PROCEDURE

1. Distribute reproducible Umpire to each student.

2. Have students look at the picture of the umpire and find the hidden numbers.

3. Once the hidden numbers have been located by all students, distribute the reproducible Addition Problems and instruct students to complete the problems. Have students turn in their solutions or hold a class discussion on the results. (See Answer Key, page 152.)

4. Repeat step 3 with the reproducible Subtraction Problems. (See Answer Key, page 152.)

5. Repeat step 3 with the reproducible Multiplication Problems. (See Answer Key, page 153.)

EXTENSIONS AND ADAPTATIONS

1. Instead of using the reproducibles, orally present the problems and let students use mental math and volunteer answers.

2. The picture of the umpire could be used to set up fractions and proportions, for example:

   a. Does $\dfrac{\text{right shoulder}}{\text{fingers}} = \dfrac{\text{fingers}}{\text{ear}}$?

   b. What does $\dfrac{\text{hat}}{\text{eyes}} + \dfrac{\text{fingers}}{\text{eyes}} = ?$

3. Make up a problem sheet utilizing all three operations.

4. Let students cut out the picture of the umpire, attach it to a larger sheet of paper, and design a background. They can finish their pictures by coloring.

5. Related activities Compare and Capture on page 14, Don't Be a Square on page 56, It's a Snap on page 58, Pick As Many As You Can on page 60, and Egg 'Em On on page 64.

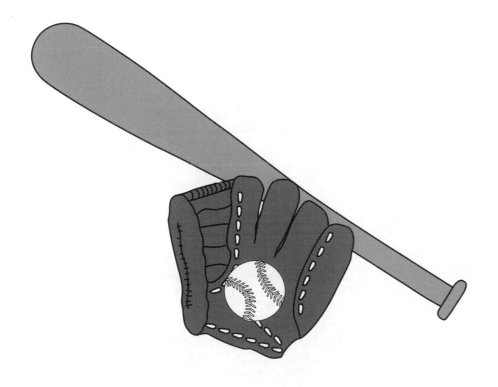

BAD CALL _____

UMPIRE

Name_____

Mathematics Activities (KSAM)

BAD CALL _____

ADDITION PROBLEMS

Name_____

Directions: Look at the picture of the umpire. Then solve the problems.

1. What would you get if you added his fingers and hat together? _____

2. What is the total of his ear added to his left arm? _____

3. What do you have to add to his left shoulder to get 15? _____

4. If you add together his hat, right shoulder, and mouth, what do you get? _____

5. What would all the numbers on his face add up to? _____

6. How much is an elbow plus an ear plus a mouth plus a left arm? _____

7. How much is 2 umpire hats? _____

8. What is the total of his eyes added to his hat? _____

9. What number is added to his nose to get 6? _____

10. What is the total of all the numbers on the umpire picture? _____

BAD CALL _____

SUBTRACTION PROBLEMS

Name_____

Directions: Look at the picture of the umpire. Then solve the problems.

1. What do you get when you subtract the umpire's fingers from his ear? _____

2. What is the difference between his eyes and his mouth?_____

3. Take an elbow away from a left shoulder. What do you get?_____

4. Take a left arm away from an ear. What do you get? _____

5. Take a nose away from a hat. What do you get? _____

6. What do you get when you subtract the highest number on the umpire's body and arms from the highest number on his head?_____

7. ear
    − hat _____
    _____

8. eyes
    − right shoulder _____
    − mouth _____

9. mouth
    − left arm _____
    − left arm _____

10. left shoulder
    − fingers _____
    − nose _____

BAD CALL _____

MULTIPLICATION PROBLEMS

Name_____

Directions: Look at the picture of the umpire. Then solve the problems.

1. What would you get if you multiplied his fingers times his elbow?_____

2. What would be the total of 5 times the umpire's mouth? _____

3. What is 4 times his right shoulder? _____

4. What would 3 times his ear total? _____

5. What is the product of the umpire's fingers times his hat? _____

6. What would be the total of 3 times his left shoulder? _____

7. What would be the product of his fingers times his elbow times his
   right shoulder? _____

8. What would be the product of his nose times his ear?_____

9. Multiply 4 hats, what is the total? _____

10. Multiply his mouth times his eyes. What do you get? _____

BOX CARS

PRIMARY CONTENT

Adding and subtracting amounts of money

PRIOR STUDENT KNOWLEDGE

Addition and subtraction skills

PRE-ACTIVITY PREPARATION

1. A few days prior to this activity, ask each student to bring to school a small toy car from home. Ask students who have more than one to bring in extra cars for students who don't have a car or for those who might forget.
2. Collect shoeboxes with lids, enough for one box per group. Cut away one end of each lid. (See illustration in step 1 of the Procedure.)
3. Copy reproducible Winner/Prize Data Sheet (page 55), one copy per group.

PROCESS SKILLS

Observing, calculating

GROUP SIZE

5–6 students

MATERIALS PER GROUP

- 1 shoebox with prepared lid
- Masking tape
- Small toy car for each student
- 1 copy of reproducible Winner/Prize Data Sheet

TEACHER INFORMATION

No special teacher information is required.

PROCEDURE

1. Push the desks to the periphery of the room to make a large racing area. Distribute materials to each group.

2. Each group should construct a starting ramp and track on the classroom floor for the big race. The starting ramp is made by resting one end of the lid on the inverted shoe box, with the cut-away end of the lid resting on the floor. (See the illustration below.) The lid should be taped to the box and to the floor for stability. The track is the floor area in front of the ramp. The starting point is at the top of the ramp, with the rear of the car against the end of the lid.

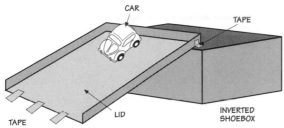

3. The race is won by the car that travels the farthest. The cars are not to be pushed, but just simply "let go." Obviously, not all students in the group can race simultaneously. Rather, students can race their cars individually or in pairs, marking (with tape and initials) the point where each car stops. Their cars are then removed and others in the group repeat the procedure until all have completed the race.

4. Each group conducts three races, recording the First Place, Second Place, and Third Place winners and their prizes for each race on the group's Winner/Prize Data Sheet. Prizes are: $1.00 for First Place, $.75 for Second Place, and $.25 for Third Place.

5. After all the groups have completed their three races, collect each group's Winner/Prize Data Sheet and record on the board the names of all prize winners and the prizes received (for example, John Doe $.25, $1.00; Jane Doe $.50; Mary Smith $.50, $1.00, $.25, etc.).

6. Now, all students who came in First Place in any of the three races will race in the Grand Finale—one race with the following prizes: $5.00 for First Place, $3.00 for Second Place, and $1.50 for Third Place.

7. At the conclusion of the Grand Finale, add the awarded prize money to the list already on the board.

8. Direct each student, using the data listed on the board, to figure:
   a. the total amount of prize money awarded in the class
   b. the most (total) given to one (or more) student(s)
   c. the least (total) given to one (or more) student(s)
   d. the difference between the most given and the least given

A variety of other manipulations can be done at your discretion.

9. Conduct a class discussion, reviewing the questions and correct responses.

EXTENSIONS AND ADAPTATIONS

1. Have students use different materials to increase the steepness of the starting ramp.

2. Use sections of old garden hose as railings to outline a raceway.

3. Related activities Show Those Fingers! on page 68, Wheel of Numbers on page 74, Let's Go Out to Eat on page 141, Pets Cost Money on page 144, and Stump 'Em on page 148.

BOX CARS _____

WINNER/PRIZE DATA SHEET

Group Number _____

Directions: Record the names of First Place, Second Place, and Third Place winners and their prizes for each race. Prizes are: $1.00 for First Place, $.75 for Second Place, and $.25 for Third Place.

Race Number 1 ▪▪▪▪▪▪▪▪▪▪▪▪▪▪▪▪▪▪▪▪▪▪

	Name	Prize
First Place	_____	_____
Second Place	_____	_____
Third Place	_____	_____

Race Number 2 ▪▪▪▪▪▪▪▪▪▪▪▪▪▪▪▪▪▪▪▪▪▪

	Name	Prize
First Placc	_____	_____
Second Place	_____	_____
Third Place	_____	_____

Race Number 3 ▪▪▪▪▪▪▪▪▪▪▪▪▪▪▪▪▪▪▪▪▪▪

	Name	Prize
First Place	_____	_____
Second Place	_____	_____
Third Place	_____	_____

DON'T BE A SQUARE

PRIMARY CONTENT

Multiplying two-digit numbers by one-digit numbers, with and without regrouping

PRIOR STUDENT KNOWLEDGE

Experience in multiplication

PRE-ACTIVITY PREPARATION

Write multiplication problems, including the answers, on 3 in. x 5 in. index cards, with each card displaying one problem. The problems should consist of two-digit numbers multiplied by one-digit numbers, with and without regrouping, as shown in the examples below.

$$
\begin{array}{cc}
36 & 13 \\
\underline{\times 5} & \underline{\times 2} \\
180 & 26
\end{array}
$$

Make enough cards to equal the number of students in the class.

PROCESS SKILLS

Observing, calculating, recording, analyzing, problem solving

GROUP SIZE

Whole class

MATERIALS PER GROUP

Multiplication cards

TEACHER INFORMATION

No special teacher information is required.

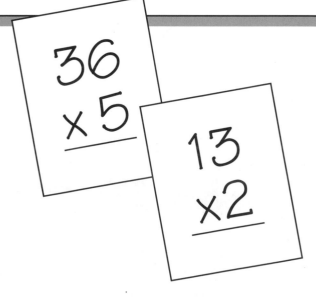

PROCEDURE

1. Draw the following on the board.

```
  - -  - - -
x         - - -
  - - - -
```

2. Select one student to be first and come to the front of the room. That student chooses a multiplication card. The card is not shown to the class.

3. Students take turns, as they are called upon, guessing a number from 0–9 to fill in the blanks. Each time a number guessed is one of the numbers in the problem on the card, that number is written in the correct blank space by the student. If the number guessed occupies more than one space in the problem, the number is shown in all appropriate places. (For example, in the problem 13 x 2 = 26, if the number 2 is guessed, it is written in both places.)

4. Guessing continues until a number not in the problem is chosen.

5. If a number guessed is not one of the numbers in the problem, the student draws one side of a square (that would contain the whole problem if the square was completed), and another student is called on for the next guess. After four incorrect responses, a square will be completed around the entire problem, and the student fills in the remaining blank spaces. The same student then chooses another multiplication card, and play continues.

6. If the numbers are filled in before the square is completed, the student who guesses the last number gets to pick the next multiplication card and repeat the procedure.

7. When a few numbers have been placed in a problem, students can begin to use strategies to figure out the other numbers. (For example, if the problem is 1 ___ x 2 = ___ 6, what number times 2 gives you 6 in the ones place? Either 3 or 8 would be the next guess.)

EXTENSIONS AND ADAPTATIONS

1. This activity can be used for any of the four basic operations.

2. Related activities Bad Call on page 46 and It's a Snap on page 58.

IT'S A SNAP

PRIMARY CONTENT
Multiplying two-digit numbers by one-digit numbers, with and without regrouping

PROCESS SKILLS
Observing, comparing, counting, measuring, recording

PRIOR STUDENT KNOWLEDGE
Multiplication facts and regrouping skills

GROUP SIZE
3 students followed by whole class

PRE-ACTIVITY PREPARATION
No special pre-activity preparation is required.

MATERIALS PER GROUP
1 stop watch or a watch with a second hand (or a room clock with a second hand for the whole class)

TEACHER INFORMATION

No special teacher information is required.

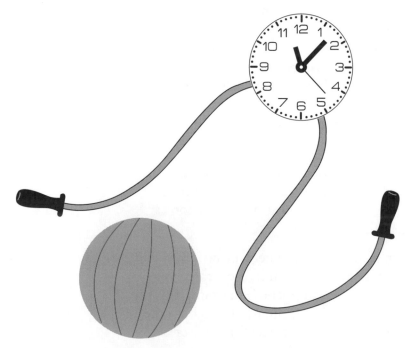

PROCEDURE

1. Divide the class into groups of three according to the activity that students choose or that you assign them.

2. Suggested activities (you or class members may suggest others):

   Activity
   snap your fingers
   bounce a ball
   jump a rope
   do jumping jacks
   do push ups
   write your name
   blink your eyes
   string a set of beads

3. Each group of three consists of a Timer, a Doer, and a Counter.

4. When the Timer says go, the Doer does the activity, and the Counter counts the number of activity repetitions for fifteen seconds (at which point the timer says stop). (Time period may be varied to fit curriculum objectives.)

5. The student's name (Doer's name) and the number of activity repetitions are recorded on the board (see step 6). Repeat the process by switching tasks until all three students have completed the activity.

6. While students are engaged in the various activities, list the activities across the board, with each activity heading a column. At the top of the columns by each activity, write x2, x3, x4, x5, etc. These numbers will serve as the multipliers. It is in these columns (under the appropriate activity) that students are to record their names and the number of activity repetitions completed in fifteen seconds. Example:

(x2) Push Ups	(x3) Bounce Ball	(x4) Jump Rope	(x5) Snap Fingers
Kim 5	Cora 13	Juan 12	Rosa 29
Theo 4	Nina 24	Ari 24	Pedro 31
Joel 6	Sean 17	Sara 44	Ella 40

7. After all the activities have been completed and the data recorded, instruct each student to select two names (number could be more or less depending on curriculum objectives) under each activity and to write a word problem for each selection by filling in the blanks:

   (*selected name*) did (*number of repetitions*) (*activity*) in 15 seconds. He/she could do (*compute answer*) in (*multiplier for that activity*) times as long.

   Example: Ella did 40 finger snaps in 15 seconds. She could do 200 in 5 times as long.

   Write the word problem setup on the board for students to copy before doing their problems.

8. Do a few examples together and then let students complete the assignment.

9. Have students regroup to check one another's answers.

EXTENSIONS AND ADAPTATIONS

1. Each student can do his/her activity once for the whole class, rather than in groups of three.

2. Related activities Bad Call on page 46 and Don't Be a Square on page 56.

PICK AS MANY AS YOU CAN _____

PRIMARY CONTENT
- Adding one-digit and two-digit numbers
- Recognizing combinations of numbers that sum to a given total

PRIOR STUDENT KNOWLEDGE
Familiarization with basic addition facts

PRE-ACTIVITY PREPARATION
Copy reproducible Playing Board (page 63), one copy per student.

PROCESS SKILLS
Observing, calculating, analyzing

GROUP SIZE
2–6 students

MATERIALS PER GROUP
- 3 conventional dice
- 19 game markers (beans, buttons) for each student
- 1 copy of reproducible Playing Board for each student

TEACHER INFORMATION
No special teacher information is required.

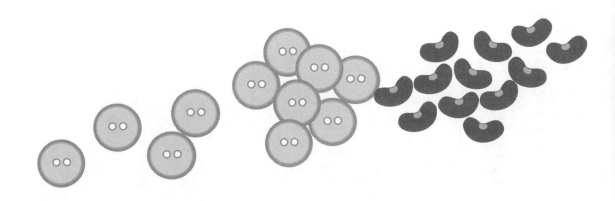

PROCEDURE

1. Distribute materials to each group.

2. Each player places a marker in each circle on his/her playing board. The value of a marker is the number displayed next to the circle on the playing board.

3. Order of play is determined by each player's role of the dice, with the highest total going first and the lowest total going last.

4. Players take turns rolling the dice and adding the numbers that result. The player must pick up the sum rolled by using the values next to the markers on the playing board. To pick up the sum, players take a marker value or a combination of marker values that add up to the same sum. For example, if the sum of the three rolled dice equals 11, the player can pick up markers 1, 2, 3, and 5; or markers 1, 3, and 7; or markers 9 and 2; or just marker 11. Obviously, strategy in deciding which addition combinations to select becomes an important element in the game.

5. There is one Wild marker. It represents any number desired.

6. Players keep their own score on a separate sheet of paper. A player scores 1 point for each marker removed and 1 point for each number used to total the sum. Using the example above, the 1, 2, 3, 5 combination scores 8 points; the 1, 3, 7 combination scores 6 points; the 9, 2 combination scores 4 points; and the 11 alone scores 2 points.

7. If a player makes a mistake in addition on a combination, those tokens are returned to their pervious positions and the player loses that turn.

8. If a player rolls and is unable to pick up any markers, that player is out of the game.

9. The game continues until each player is out of the game.

10. The winner of the game is the player who has the highest point total.

EXTENSIONS AND ADAPTATIONS

1. Have students play another version of the game. Play continues until one player has removed all of his/her markers from the playing board. This version takes a little longer.

2. This activity is appropriate for use in a learning center.

3. Related activities Compare and Capture on page 14, Bad Call on page 46, and Egg 'Em On on page 64.

PICK AS MANY AS YOU CAN _____

PLAYING BOARD

Name_____

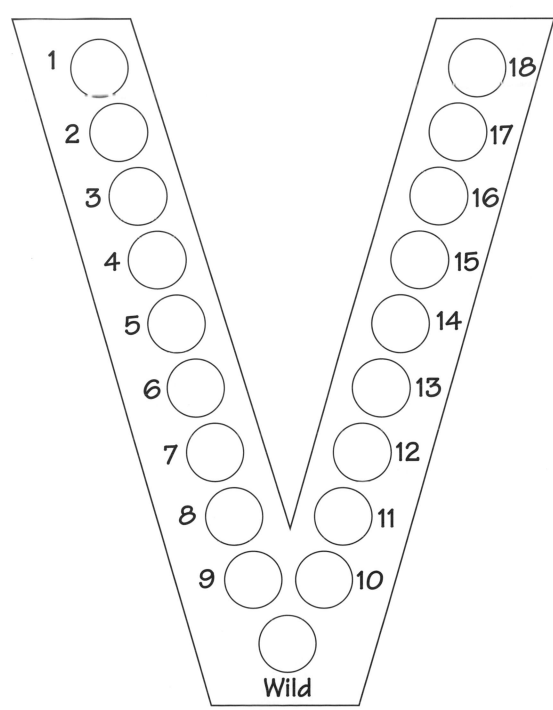

EGG 'EM ON

PRIMARY CONTENT

- Adding two-digit numbers, with and without regrouping
- Subtracting two-digit numbers, with and without regrouping
- Comparing number size

PRIOR STUDENT KNOWLEDGE

Previous experience with two-digit addition and subtraction

PRE-ACTIVITY PREPARATION

1. Collect (personally or through students) enough egg cartons to provide one carton for each group. To prepare cartons, number the egg compartments with a marker as illustrated in step 1 of the Procedure.
2. Reproducible Score Sheet (page 67) provides two score sheets. Make enough copies for you to cut out one Score Sheet for each student.

PROCESS SKILLS

Observing, comparing, calculating, recording

GROUP SIZE

2–4 students

MATERIALS PER GROUP

- 1 egg carton
- 1 lima bean
- 1 navy bean
- 1 copy of reproducible Score Sheet for each student

TEACHER INFORMATION

No special teacher information is required.

PROCEDURE

1. Distribute the materials to each group. An opened egg carton will look like the one illustrated below.

2. Each player takes a turn placing one bean in the carton, closing the lid, and shaking the carton. Order of play is determined by the resulting numbers, with the highest going first and the lowest going last. Each player's turn consists of two shakes, and a game consists of six turns per player.

3. To play the game:

   a. The player places both beans (the large lima bean and the small navy bean) inside the egg carton. The large bean identifies the tens digit, while the small bean identifies the ones digit.

   b. The player closes the lid of the carton and shakes the carton. That player then opens the carton and observes the numbers in the compartments where the two beans have landed, combining the tens digit and the ones digit into a single two-digit number. For example, if the lima bean landed in the 7 compartment and the navy bean landed in the 4 compartment, the resulting two-digit number would be 74.

   c. The student writes that two-digit number on his/her Score Sheet in the first blank inside the parentheses that follow the turn number.

   d. The process is then repeated for the player's second shake for that turn. The player writes the second two-digit number in the second blank inside the parentheses.

   e. Next the player writes the larger of the two numbers in the Larger Number column and the smaller of the two numbers in the Smaller Number column. Then the player completes the indicated operation (either addition or subtraction, depending on the turn number).

   f. Play then moves to the next player, who repeats steps b–e; then to the next player and so on.

4. After six turns, each player figures out his/her Total Score. Score Sheets are then exchanged for checking. If a student has made any errors in addition or subtraction, the student must correct the errors, and 10 points for each error is deducted from that player's Total Score. The player with the highest Final Score wins.

EXTENSIONS AND ADAPTATIONS

1. This activity is appropriate for use in a learning center.

2. Fractions can be used instead of whole numbers.

3. Related activities Bad Call on page 46 and Pick As Many As You Can on page 60.

EGG 'EM ON _____

SCORE SHEET

Name _____

		Larger Number		Smaller Number		Score
Turn 1	(_____ _____):	_____	+	_____	=	_____
Turn 2	(_____ _____):	_____	−	_____	=	_____
Turn 3	(_____ _____):	_____	+	_____	=	_____
Turn 4	(_____ _____):	_____	−	_____	=	_____
Turn 5	(_____ _____):	_____	+	_____	=	_____
Turn 6	(_____ _____):	_____	−	_____	=	_____

TOTAL SCORE   =   _____

Number of errors _____ x 10   =   ⁻ _____

FINAL SCORE   =   _____

SCORE SHEET

Name _____

		Larger Number		Smaller Number		Score
Turn 1	(_____ _____):	_____	+	_____	=	_____
Turn 2	(_____ _____):	_____	−	_____	=	_____
Turn 3	(_____ _____):	_____	+	_____	=	_____
Turn 4	(_____ _____):	_____	−	_____	=	_____
Turn 5	(_____ _____):	_____	+	_____	=	_____
Turn 6	(_____ _____):	_____	−	_____	=	_____

TOTAL SCORE   =   _____

Number of errors _____ x 10   =   ⁻ _____

FINAL SCORE   =   _____

SHOW THOSE FINGERS! _____

PRIMARY CONTENT

- Reading and writing three-digit and four-digit numbers
- Adding three-digit numbers, with and without regrouping

PRIOR STUDENT KNOWLEDGE

Left-to-right progression of numbers; recognition of three-digit numbers

PRE-ACTIVITY PREPARATION

Cut answer strips out of scrap paper. Answer strips should be approximately 3 in. x 4 in. Cut enough so that each student gets four or five answer strips.

PROCESS SKILLS

Observing, classifying, calculating

GROUP SIZE

Whole class divided into 2 groups (teams)

MATERIALS PER GROUP

4–5 answer strips for each student

TEACHER INFORMATION

No special teacher information is required.

PROCEDURE

1. Divide the class into two teams, with one team sitting at desks in the right half of the room and the other team sitting at desks in the left half. All desks should be facing the front of the room.

2. Give answer strips to each student.

3. Select three Number Makers from each team. Have each group of Number Makers stand shoulder-to-shoulder in the front of the room, facing their team.

4. When you say "show those fingers," each Number Maker should hold up the number of fingers from 1–9 that he/she wishes.

5. Each team will now have a three-digit number which is represented by the fingers that are held up by the team's Number Makers. The numbers will be in left-to-right progression as viewed by students at their desks.

6. Students should write both team numbers (represented by the fingers) on one of their answer strips, writing one number under the other so that the two numbers are lined up for addition.

   For example, if on **Team One:**
   > Student A holds up 6 fingers,
   > Student B holds up 3 fingers,
   > Student C holds up 2 fingers,

   and on **Team Two:**
   > Student A holds up 3 fingers,
   > Student B holds up 9 fingers,
   > Student C holds up 7 fingers,

   then, students should write the following, remembering to use left-to-right progression.

$$\begin{array}{r} 632 \\ + 397 \\ \hline \end{array}$$

7. Students then add the two three-digit numbers. When each student has the answer, he/she holds the strip of paper to his/her forehead so that no other students can see the answer.

8. After a predetermined amount of time, have students show their answers. Two points are awarded to the first two students (regardless of team) who wrote the correct answer and put the strip to their forehead.

9. You serve as judge, checker, and scorekeeper.

10. Repeat the process with three new Number Makers from each team.

11. Continue playing until each student has been a Number Maker at least once. The team with the highest score wins.

EXTENSIONS AND ADAPTATIONS

1. Have students subtract or multiply the two numbers.

2. If desired, the number of digits (Number Makers) can be increased or decreased for any of the operations to better address curriculum objectives.

3. Related activities Box Cars on page 52, Wheel of Numbers on page 74, Let's Go Out to Eat on page 141, Pets Cost Money on page 144, and Stump 'Em on page 148.

SNIP A GRID

PRIMARY CONTENT
Dividing, using one-digit divisors

PRIOR STUDENT KNOWLEDGE
Multiplication facts up to 5 x 9

PRE-ACTIVITY PREPARATION
1. Copy reproducible Problem Sheet (page 72), one copy per student.
2. Copy reproducible Grid Sheet (page 73), a minimum of three copies per student. The number of additional copies depends on the number of items students complete on their own. (See step 11 in the Procedure.)

PROCESS SKILLS
Observing, comparing, counting, calculating, recording, inferring

GROUP SIZE
Individual

MATERIALS PER GROUP
- 1 pair of scissors
- 1 copy of reproducible Problem Sheet
- 3 copies (minimum) of reproducible Grid Sheet
- Crayons

TEACHER INFORMATION

No special teacher information is required.

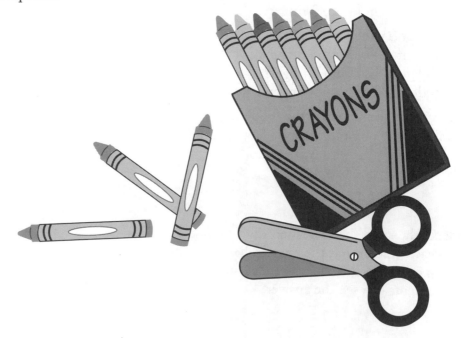

PROCEDURE

1. Distribute materials (only one copy of the Grid Sheet at this time) to each student.

2. Ask students to count out (or determine) an area that has 20 squares in it. (The area does not need to be a rectangle but should be contiguous.)

3. Tell students to outline the area with a blue crayon and then color the whole area (the 20 squares) blue.

4. When they have finished coloring, have students cut out the blue region.

5. Continue with a dialogue similar to the following:
   - How many times does 5 divide 20?
   - Find out by taking your blue region (which has 20 squares) and cutting away a section of 5 squares, then another section of 5 squares, and so on until you only have one 5-square section left.
   - Now count the number of 5-square sections (sets) you have.
   - How many sets are there?
   - Then 5 goes into 20 four times.
   - Find 20 ÷ 5 on your Problem Sheet (item 25) and record the answer.

6. Tell students to put away all the blue sections and give each student another Grid Sheet.

7. This time have students use a yellow crayon to outline an area that has 12 squares. As previously, they are to color the entire area (12 squares) yellow and then cut out the entire yellow area.

8. Repeat step 5, asking students to figure out how many times 4 divides 12, ending with students each recording the answer to item 11 on their Problem Sheet.

9. If desired, walk through another example using 18 ÷ 3 and a third Grid Sheet.

10. Ask students to look for patterns in the division problems and answers.

11. Identify the number of items on the Problem sheet that you wish students to complete. Then distribute the appropriate number of Grid Sheets to each student. Have students complete the items on their own, using the process demonstrated in the examples.

EXTENSIONS AND ADAPTATIONS

1. Have students use the colored pieces to determine further divisions. (For example, 8 ÷ 4 = 2; then use each piece of 4 to find how many times 2 goes into 8 by cutting the 4s into 2s.)

2. Provide some dividends that will produce remainders. (For example, 23 ÷ 5 = 4 pieces of 5 and 3 left over.)

3. Have students work with areas of more than 45 total squares.

4. This activity is appropriate for use in a learning center.

SNIP A GRID _____

PROBLEM SHEET

Name _____

1. 4 ÷ 2 = _____

2. 6 ÷ 2 = _____

3. 6 ÷ 3 = _____

4. 8 ÷ 2 = _____

5. 8 ÷ 4 = _____

6. 9 ÷ 3 = _____

7. 10 ÷ 2 = _____

8. 10 ÷ 5 = _____

9. 12 ÷ 2 = _____

10. 12 ÷ 3 = _____

11. 12 ÷ 4 = _____

12. 12 ÷ 6 = _____

13. 14 ÷ 2 = _____

14. 14 ÷ 7 = _____

15. 15 ÷ 3 = _____

16. 15 ÷ 5 = _____

17. 16 ÷ 2 = _____

18. 16 ÷ 4 = _____

19. 16 ÷ 8 = _____

20. 18 ÷ 2 = _____

21. 18 ÷ 3 = _____

22. 18 ÷ 6 = _____

23. 18 ÷ 9 = _____

24. 20 ÷ 4 = _____

25. 20 ÷ 5 = _____

26. 21 ÷ 3 = _____

27. 21 ÷ 7 = _____

28. 24 ÷ 3 = _____

29. 24 ÷ 4 = _____

30. 24 ÷ 6 = _____

31. 24 ÷ 8 = _____

32. 25 ÷ 5 = _____

33. 27 ÷ 3 = _____

34. 27 ÷ 9 = _____

35. 28 ÷ 4 = _____

36. 28 ÷ 7 = _____

37. 30 ÷ 5 = _____

38. 30 ÷ 6 = _____

39. 32 ÷ 4 = _____

40. 32 ÷ 8 = _____

41. 35 ÷ 5 = _____

42. 35 ÷ 7 = _____

43. 36 ÷ 4 = _____

44. 36 ÷ 9 = _____

45. 40 ÷ 5 = _____

46. 40 ÷ 8 = _____

47. 45 ÷ 5 = _____

48. 45 ÷ 9 = _____

SNIP A GRID

GRID SHEET

Name

WHEEL OF NUMBERS

PRIMARY CONTENT

Supplying the missing numbers in one-step number sentences using addition and subtraction

PRIOR STUDENT KNOWLEDGE

Basic addition and subtraction facts

PRE-ACTIVITY PREPARATION

1. Using paper plates (or poster board or construction paper), make twenty-four number/symbol signs. On twenty-one of the signs, write the numbers 0–20, one number per sign. On three of the signs, write the symbols +, –, =, one symbol per sign.

2. Make a spinner from another paper plate or poster board, using an arrow cut from poster board and attached with a paper fastener. Divide the spinner into eight sections, each section marked with one of the following: Free Spin, Double Your Money, Lose a Turn, 5¢, 10¢, 25¢, 50¢, $1.00. Color and decorate the spinner as desired.

3. (Optional) Write twenty to thirty addition/subtraction equations on 3 in. x 5 in. index cards for use during the game. Use no number larger than 20. (Examples: 15 – 3 = 12; 8 + 9 = 17; 19 – 11 = 8; etc.) Each number, 0–20, can be used only once in each equation.

PROCESS SKILLS

Observing, calculating, inferring, predicting

GROUP SIZE

Whole class

MATERIALS PER GROUP

- 24 number/symbol signs
- 1 spinner
- (Optional) 20–30 addition/subtraction equation cards

TEACHER INFORMATION

No special teacher information is required.

PROCEDURE

1. This game proceeds much like a popular TV game show. Think of, or select from optional equation cards, an addition or subtraction equation (for example, 15 − 3 = 12). Inform students that the equation selected has either an addition or subtraction sign and does not contain any number larger than 20.

2. Select five students, one to hold each number and symbol in the equation, and provide them with the appropriate number/symbol signs. Have these five students sit in chairs, side-by-side, at the front of the room, facing the class. They should hold the signs facedown in their laps so the class cannot see what is written on them. Before play begins, the student with the equal sign turns the sign faceup so the class can see it.

3. Choose four more students: two Contestants, one Announcer, and one Scorekeeper.

4. The first Contestant spins the spinner, and the Announcer tells the result of the spin (for example, 50¢). The Contestant then guesses what might be behind one of the signs held by the seated students. If the guess is on any one of the hidden signs, the sign is held faceup, the Contestant (in this case) has 50¢, which is recorded by the Scorekeeper, and the Contestant continues to guess. If the Contestant's guess is not on one of the signs, it is the other Contestant's turn.

5. If the equation is completed during a Contestant's turn, that Contestant receives an extra 75¢. If the guess is incorrect, the other contestant receives the 75¢.

6. Free Spin can be used immediately or saved for a later time. If Double Your Money is spun before a player has any money, the doubling should occur with the first money that the player does spin.

7. The game is over when the equation is completed. The Contestant who has accumulated the most money is the winner.

8. As a reward, the winner can stay to compete against a new Contestant, or you may choose two new students for the next competition. Choose five other students to hold the signs and two other students to be Announcer and Scorekeeper.

EXTENSIONS AND ADAPTATIONS

1. Include multiplication and division equations.

2. Include equations that use less than (<) and greater than (>) in addition to the equal sign.

3. Include two-step number sentences such as 12 + 7 − 3 = 16.

4. You may want to use play money to pay students after each game is completed. Then allow students to purchase items at a class store.

5. For more advanced students, include equations that use fractions and decimals.

6. Groups of nine students can play the game instead of the whole class. Students take turns playing the different roles.

7. Related activities Box Cars on page 52, Show Those Fingers! on page 68, Let's Go Out to Eat on page 141, Pets Cost Money on page 144, and Stump 'Em on page 148.

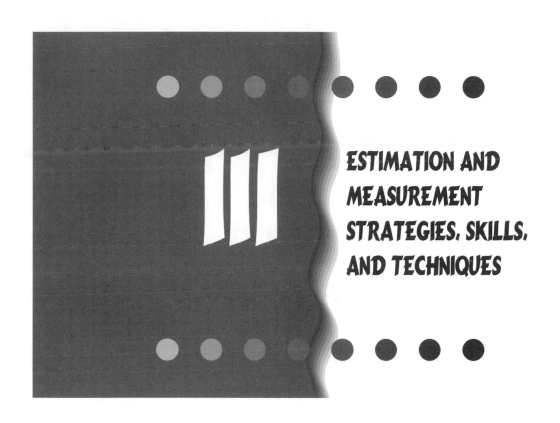

ESTIMATION AND MEASUREMENT STRATEGIES, SKILLS, AND TECHNIQUES

NOW AND LATER

PRIMARY CONTENT

Telling and recording time by five-minute intervals using a standard clock

PRIOR STUDENT KNOWLEDGE

Experience in telling time

PRE-ACTIVITY PREPARATION

Using 3 in. x 5 in. index cards, make a deck of time-change cards. A deck consists of ten to twenty-five cards indicating time changes such as: 3 hours later, $1\frac{1}{4}$ hours later, 6 hours and 25 minutes later, 35 minutes later, 8 hours and 15 minutes later, etc.

PROCESS SKILLS

Observing, comparing, measuring

GROUP SIZE

Whole class

MATERIALS PER GROUP

- 2 clock faces (from school supply company if not part of classroom supplies)
- 1 deck of time-change cards

TEACHER INFORMATION

No special teacher information is required.

PROCEDURE

1. Select two students to be Clock Holders, two students to be Clock Setters, and two students to be Time Tellers. These six students come to the front of the room, face the class, and form two groups. Each group has one Clock Holder, one Clock Setter, and one Time Teller. Each Clock Holder is given a clock face.

2. In the first group, the Time Teller asks the Clock Setter to set the clock at any given time (on a five-minute interval, for example: 2:50, 8:05, 11:15, etc.). If needed, the Clock Setter may ask for assistance from the other two members of the group. The class checks the set clock for correctness.

3. Next, the Time Teller in the second group selects a time-change card and instructs the Clock Setter in the first group to figure out and display the new time. Again, assistance may be provided by the other two group members.

4. The class checks the changed time for accuracy.

5. The same two groups play a second round. In this round, the order of the tasks are reversed. (The group that originated the time in the first round must now respond to a time-change card.)

6. Six new students are chosen and the activity proceeds until each student has participated.

EXTENSIONS AND ADAPTATIONS

1. Cards can be made up to indicate time before, such as $3\frac{1}{4}$ hours before; 2 hours and 50 minutes before; etc.

2. The activity can be done with mixed time cards—some indicating time before and others indicating time after.

HOW MANY PENNIES EQUAL A NICKEL? _____

PRIMARY CONTENT
- Comparative weight measurement
- Simple problems using proportions

PRIOR STUDENT KNOWLEDGE
No special prior knowledge is required.

PRE-ACTIVITY PREPARATION
No special pre-activity preparation is required.

PROCESS SKILLS
Observing, comparing, measuring, calculating, predicting

GROUP SIZE
2 students

MATERIALS PER GROUP
- 1 ruler (with a flat side)
- 1 domino (or appropriate substitute)
- Masking tape (for entire class)
- 4 nickels
- 10 pennies

TEACHER INFORMATION

Pennies dated 1984 or later are a different weight than those minted earlier. This may be a cause of some variation of data between groups.

PROCEDURE

1. Get the class ready for the activity by asking questions such as:

   - How many pennies equal one nickel?

   - Can you think of any other ways to compare pennies to nickels? (Size and weight are the most obvious.)

   - How many pennies will it take to equal one nickel in weight? (All students should record their predictions on a sheet of paper.)

2. Distribute materials to each group.

3. Have each group construct a balance beam using the ruler and domino. (See illustration below.) Taping the domino on both sides to a desk or table will add stability. Tell each group to be sure that it is the flat side of the ruler that is placed on the domino. A twelve-inch ruler should balance by placing the six-inch mark at the center of the fulcrum (domino).

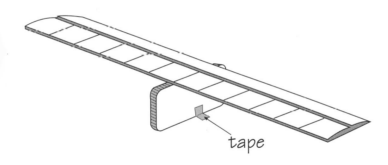

tape

4. Ask students to place one nickel on one end of the ruler and balance it with stacked pennies on the other end. Have students record how many pennies equal a nickel in terms of weight. Then ask them to compare this measurement with their estimates. (Depending on objectives, you may or may not want to caution students that the coins must be in the same position at both ends of the ruler; otherwise, another variable has been added—distance to the fulcrum. The problem can be avoided, if desired, by telling students that, at both ends of the ruler, the outer edge of the coin(s) must be even with the end of the ruler.)

5. Give the following instructions to complete the activity:

   a. Double the number of coins on each end. Is the ruler still in balance?

   b. Can you determine, just through calculations, how many pennies it would take to balance four nickels? After you have made your calculations, do that measurement to see if you are correct.

   c. How many pennies will it take to balance $1 worth of nickels? See if you can figure it out.

6. Conduct a class discussion of results, perhaps summarizing them in a table on the board. Let different groups share how they did their calculations for 5b and 5c. If there are variations in actual measurements among the groups, ask students to think of ways those variations might be explained.

EXTENSIONS AND ADAPTATIONS

1. Use two other coins, such as dimes and quarters or pennies and dimes.

2. This activity is appropriate for use in a learning center.

CENTI'ME'TER _____

PRIMARY CONTENT	PROCESS SKILLS

PRIMARY CONTENT

Estimating and measuring lengths using the metric system

PRIOR STUDENT KNOWLEDGE

Skill in reading a ruler; basic understanding of metric units

PRE-ACTIVITY PREPARATION

Copy reproducible Student Data Sheet (page 85), one copy per student.

PROCESS SKILLS

Observing, comparing, measuring, estimating, recording

GROUP SIZE

2–4 students

MATERIALS PER GROUP

- 1 copy of reproducible Student Data Sheet for each student
- 1 meterstick or metric measuring tape
- 1 roll of masking tape (for whole class)

TEACHER INFORMATION

No special teacher information is required.

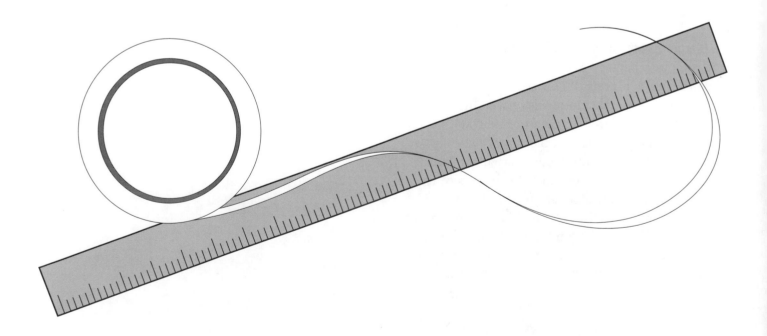

PROCEDURE

1. Distribute materials to each group.

2. Have students estimate in centimeters the lengths of the indicated body parts and areas. Have students record their estimates on their Student Data Sheets. (Enhancing student skills in metric estimation is the primary focus of this activity.)

3. Move desks to the periphery of the room to create a large area of floor space for students to measure.

4. Now have students take actual measurements and record them on their Student Data Sheets.

5. The simplest procedure for doing this is to have the student who is being measured lie down on the floor. His/Her group partner(s) will then, using the illustration on the Student Data Sheet as a guide, mark on the floor with strips of masking tape the length to be measured. The student can then get up, and the actual measurement can be made by measuring the distance between the two tape strips. (Because it decreases the chance of error and confusion regarding whose strip is whose and what strips represent what lengths, it is better if only one length [for example, height] is marked and measured at a time, with these tape strips being removed and discarded prior to the next measurement.)

6. After students have completed the activity, conduct a class discussion of the results.

EXTENSIONS AND ADAPTATIONS

1. Let students estimate and measure other body dimensions. (fingers, hand span, etc.)

2. Have students estimate and measure selected dimensions/objects in the classroom.

3. Have students measure common dimensions/objects at home and bring measurements to school for comparisons.

4. This activity is appropriate for use in a learning center.

5. Related activities Face It on page 86 and Measure Up on page 88.

CENTI'ME'TER _____

STUDENT DATA SHEET

Name_____

HEIGHT

Est. _____

Meas. _____

Est. _____

Meas. _____

ARM SPAN

ARM LENGTH

Est. _____

Meas. _____

LEG LENGTH

Est. _____

Meas. _____

Est. _____

FOOT LENGTH

Meas. _____

FACE IT

PRIMARY CONTENT
Measuring lengths in centimeters

PRIOR STUDENT KNOWLEDGE
Skill in reading a ruler; basic understanding of metric units

PRE-ACTIVITY PREPARATION
Copy reproducible Mystery Metric Message (page 87), one copy per student.

PROCESS SKILLS
Observing, measuring, recording, interpreting

GROUP SIZE
Individual

MATERIALS PER GROUP
• 1 metric ruler
• 1 copy of reproducible Mystery Metric Message

TEACHER INFORMATION

No special teacher information is required.

PROCEDURE

1. Introduce the activity by asking the class if they know what codes are. Briefly discuss codes, perhaps giving a few examples. (Morse code is probably the most famous.) Tell students that today they are going to decipher a mystery message written in metric code.

2. Distribute materials to each student. Point out that the key to the code is given at the top of the reproducible.

3. Instruct students to look at item 1 and to measure the first line segment in centimeters. Have students record that length above the first line. (It is 13 cm.) Then tell students to measure the second line segment and to record the length above the line. (It is 1 cm.)

4. Now have students look at the code and find 13 cm (13 cm = M) and 1 cm (1 cm = A).

5. Have students write M in the blank next to the 13 cm line segment and A in the blank next to the 1 cm line segment.

6. Instruct students to follow the same procedure to complete items 1–3.

7. When students have finished, they can arrange the words in order from items 1–3 to form the sentence: MAKE A FACE. Tell students to write the sentence at the bottom of the sheet.

8. Divide students into groups of three or four and have them write messages using line segments using the code.

9. Let the groups exchange messages and decode them.

EXTENSIONS AND ADAPTATIONS

1. Have students send messages to other students using this method.

2. Have students write spelling words in line segments using the code.

3. Write messages to students throughout the year using this code.

4. This activity is appropriate for use in a learning center.

5. Related activities Centi'Me'ter on page 82 and Measure Up on page 88.

FACE IT

MYSTERY METRIC MESSAGE

Name _____

A = 1 cm	H = 8 cm	O = 15 cm	V = 22 cm
B = 2 cm	I = 9 cm	P = 16 cm	W = 23 cm
C = 3 cm	J = 10 cm	Q = 17 cm	X = 24 cm
D = 4 cm	K = 11 cm	R = 18 cm	Y = 25 cm
E = 5 cm	L = 12 cm	S = 19 cm	Z = 26 cm
F = 6 cm	M = 13 cm	T = 20 cm	
G = 7 cm	N = 14 cm	U = 21 cm	

1. ├──────────────────────────────┤ _____

   ├──┤ _____

   ├───────────────────────────┤ _____

   ├────────────┤ _____

2. ├──┤ _____

3. ├───────────────┤ _____

   ├──┤ _____

   ├─────────┤ _____

   ├────────────┤ _____

MEASURE UP

PRIMARY CONTENT

Estimating and measuring lengths to the nearest inch and/or centimeter

PRIOR STUDENT KNOWLEDGE

Skill in reading a ruler

PRE-ACTIVITY PREPARATION

1. Copy reproducible Student Data Sheet (page 93), one copy per student.
2. Depending on objectives, copy reproducible Customary Measurement (page 90) and/or Metric Measurement (page 91), one copy per student.

PROCESS SKILLS

Observing, comparing, measuring, estimating, recording

GROUP SIZE

Individual

MATERIALS PER GROUP

- 1 customary ruler or metric ruler
- 1 copy of reproducible Customary Measurement
- 1 copy of reproducible Metric Measurement
- Crayons
- 1 large sheet of drawing paper
- 1 copy of reproducible Student Data Sheet

TEACHER INFORMATION

Measure Up enhances the measuring skills of students. The inclusion of two different figure sheets (pages 90–91) allows Measure Up to be completed using either customary units (inches) or metric units (centimeters), depending on curriculum objectives. If measuring practice using both systems is desired, it is recommended that students progress completely through the activity using one system and then repeat the activity with the other system. This separation helps minimize student confusion during the measuring process. It is also helpful to inexperienced students if you use rulers with only inch increments (not fractions thereof) and centimeter increments (not millimeters), if such are available. The use of standard rulers, however, is certainly acceptable.

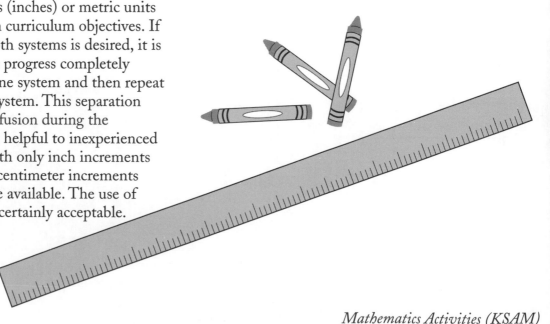

PROCEDURE

1. Distribute materials to each student.

2. Have each student measure the sides of the figures on the reproducible to the nearest inch or centimeter (depending on which reproducible is used). Take time to compare answers when students are finished. (See Answer Key, page 153.)

3. Now give students four measurements to use and have them make a five-sided figure on the drawing paper using those four measurements plus another of their own choosing. Let them color the figure and the background as they wish.

4. Instruct students to exchange the drawings made in step 3 so that they can check each other's measurements.

5. Write on the board a numbered list of items in the room that can be measured with the rulers (length of a reading book or length of a new pencil, for example).

6. Have students use the reproducible Student Data Sheet to write the same list of items and the estimates of all the lengths.

7. Record at least some of the estimates next to the appropriate items on the board. Discuss the range of estimates with students.

8. Select students to measure one item at a time. Write the actual measurements on the board next to each item and direct students to record the actual measurements on their Student Data Sheets. Make it clear to students that measurement using rulers is an approximation and is never truly exact.

EXTENSIONS AND ADAPTATIONS

1. Let students make a bar graph of the estimates of the different items listed on the board in step 5 of the Procedure. The actual measurements can be represented by a bar of a different color.

2. Have students measure items outside the classroom using meters, feet, and yards.

3. Related activities Centi'Me'ter on page 82 and Face It on page 86.

MEASURE UP

CUSTOMARY MEASUREMENT

Name_____

_____ in.

_____ in.   _____ in.

_____ in.   _____ in.

_____ in.

_____ in.   _____ in.

_____ in.   _____ in.

_____ in.   _____ in.

_____ in.   _____ in.

_____ in.   _____ in.

_____ in.

MEASURE UP

METRIC MEASUREMENT

Name_____

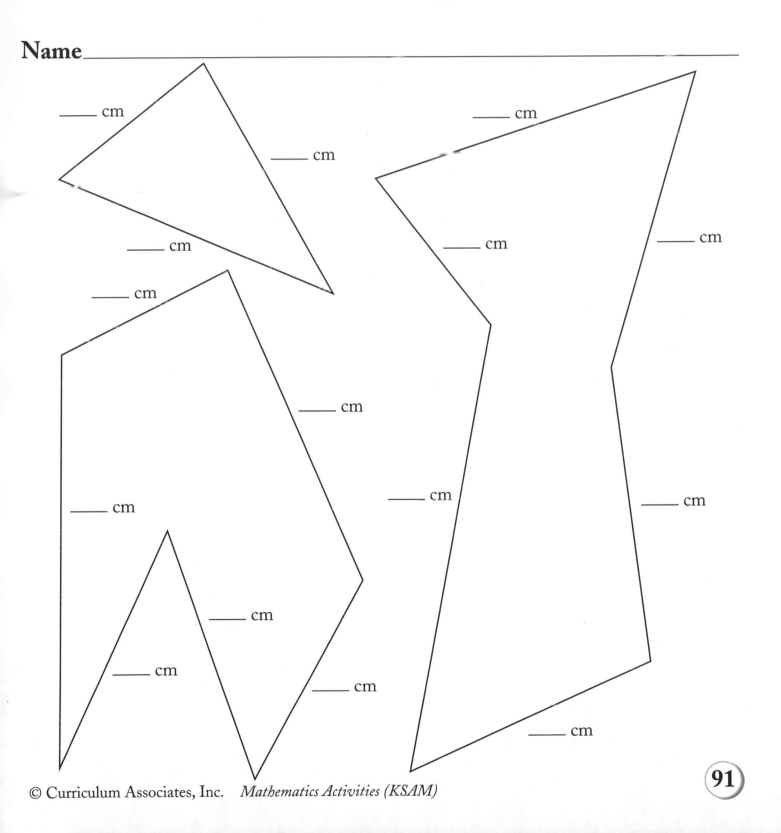

_____ cm

_____ cm

_____ cm

_____ cm

_____ cm

_____ cm

_____ cm

_____ cm

_____ cm

_____ cm

_____ cm

_____ cm

_____ cm

_____ cm

_____ cm

_____ cm

Mathematics Activities (KSAM)

MEASURE UP _____

STUDENT DATA SHEET

Name _____

	NAME OF ITEM	ESTIMATE	MEASUREMENT
1.			
2.			
3.			
4.			
5.			
6.			
7.			
8.			

RECORD A TEMP _____

PRIMARY CONTENT

Recording and graphing daily temperature for one month

PRIOR STUDENT KNOWLEDGE

The ability to read a thermometer; previous graphing experience

PRE-ACTIVITY PREPARATION

1. Using the reproducible Daily Temperature Chart (page 97) as a guide, construct a large, classroom-size daily temperature chart on poster board. The days of the month can be indicated numerically in the small, upper-left boxes.
2. Copy reproducibles Daily Temperature Chart (page 97) and Monthly Temperature Graph (page 98), one copy of each per student.

PROCESS SKILLS

Observing, comparing, measuring, gathering, recording, graphing, analyzing, interpreting

GROUP SIZE

Whole class

MATERIALS PER GROUP

- 1 classroom-size daily temperature chart (for whole class)
- 1 Fahrenheit thermometer (for whole class)
- 1 copy of reproducible Daily Temperature Chart for each student
- 1 copy of reproducible Monthly Temperature Graph for each student

TEACHER INFORMATION

1. A thermometer is an instrument used to measure air temperature. Inside the thermometer bulb is a liquid (mercury or alcohol). When the liquid is heated by warmer air through conduction, the liquid will expand and rise in the tube. When the liquid is cooled by conductive loss of heat to cooler surrounding air, the liquid will contract and fall.

The primary control of air temperature is the amount of solar energy received at the location where the temperature reading is taken. There are, however, a number of secondary controls that may cause temperature to deviate. Examples of such deviations include: an unusually warm day in winter or cold day in summer, the high for the day occurring in the morning rather than the afternoon, and temperatures near buildings being different than temperatures in the open. Because of such secondary influences, seasonal trends in temperature (such as the cooling with approaching winter or the warming with approaching summer) often do not show up on day-to-day temperature comparisons but rather become apparent only with longer-term observations of a month or more. It is also because of secondary influences that daily temperature measurements should be taken at the same location and at the same time each day.

2. Saturdays and Sundays create an apparent problem in this type of investigation. Neither you nor your students are present at school on these days to take the temperature readings in the prescribed place at the prescribed time. Actually, this turns out to be a benefit rather than a problem because it illustrates an occurrence typical in many scientific investigations at the professional level. For a multitude of reasons (equipment failure, weather conditions, human error, uncooperative subjects, missing samples, etc.), professional scientists often experience missing data in their research. Sometimes the missing data can be handled or accounted for using statistical techniques. At other times, different approaches are called for. In this activity, the following three approaches are suggested for handling the missing Saturday and Sunday data:

a. leave as missing data, connecting Friday's and Monday's points on the graph with a straight line (this may or may not accurately represent the weekend temperatures)

b. leave as missing data and do not connect Friday's and Monday's points on the graph with a line, resulting in a discontinuous line

c. based on TV and radio weather reports, fill in Saturdays and Sundays with area temperatures as opposed to school-site readings (while not perfect, the temperatures will most probably be fairly close to those at the school site)

This last approach is the one most strongly recommended, while the first approach is least recommended. It is also strongly suggested that this entire discussion on missing data be shared with the class.

PROCEDURE

1. Introduce the activity by asking students such questions as:

   • What instrument do we use to tell how warm or cold the air may be?

   • If we wanted to compare the temperatures taken on thirty different days, how could we remember what the temperatures were on each of those days?

   • If only one temperature reading is taken on each of those thirty days, should we take the temperature the same time each day? Why?

   • Should we take the temperature at the same location each day for a fair comparison? Why?

2. Tell students that they are going to be meteorologists—scientists who study the weather—during the next month, taking and recording and examining air temperature on a daily basis.

3. Display and explain the classroom chart that will be used for recording daily temperatures. Include an explanation as to how the missing data for Saturdays and Sundays is to be handled. (See Teacher Information, item 2.) Indicate that each individual student will also be given a Daily Temperature Chart so that he/she can keep a record of the temperature changes.

4. Discuss with students how to use a thermometer to take temperature readings. Warn them against touching the thermometer bulb.

5. Give each student a Daily Temperature Chart.

6. Select two different students each day to take the thermometer outdoors to read the temperature at the same time and the same place (use a shaded area to obtain consistent readings). The students should be sure to allow the thermometer time to adjust to the outdoor temperature (approximately five minutes).

7. The returning students will share the temperature reading with the class and record the temperature on the class chart. The class members will each record the temperature reading on their individual temperature charts.

8. At the end of the month, distribute a Monthly Temperature Graph to each student. Have students each graph their data using a line graph. Ask students what the advantage is of graphing the information.

9. Hold a class discussion on chart/graph results. What does that information tell us? Are any trends apparent? Why? Point out how presenting the data in graph form makes for easier interpretation because trends and changes become visually apparent.

10. Additional end-of-the-month questions might include:
    * On what day did we get the lowest reading?
    * On what day did we get the highest reading?
    * Why do weather forecasters keep records of the temperature for a long time?
    * Is there a trend developing in the weather?
    * Compare the first week in the month to the last week in the month; are there major differences?

EXTENSIONS AND ADAPTATIONS

1. Have students record the morning and evening temperatures at home for two weeks. If a thermometer is not available to them at home, they may use local radio or television temperature reports. Students should record and graph their findings. Discuss the results in class. (For example, morning vs. evening, day to day, week to week, unusual trends, etc.)

2. Have students keep a record of the daily temperature (at a given time) for several months. Graph the results. Decide if any observable patterns are presented.

3. Related activity A Hairy Graph on page 116.

RECORD A TEMP _____

DAILY TEMPERATURE CHART

Name _____   Month _____

High Temperature for Month _____   Low Temperature for Month _____

SUNDAY	MONDAY	TUESDAY	WEDNESDAY	THURSDAY	FRIDAY	SATURDAY

RECORD A TEMP

Name _____

MONTHLY TEMPERATURE GRAPH

Month _____

TEMPERATURE (°F)

100°
95°
90°
85°
80°
75°
70°
65°
60°
55°
50°
45°
40°
35°
30°
25°
20°
15°
10°
5°
0°

1 2 3 4 5 6 7 8 9 10 11 12 13 14 15 16 17 18 19 20 21 22 23 24 25 26 27 28 29 30 31

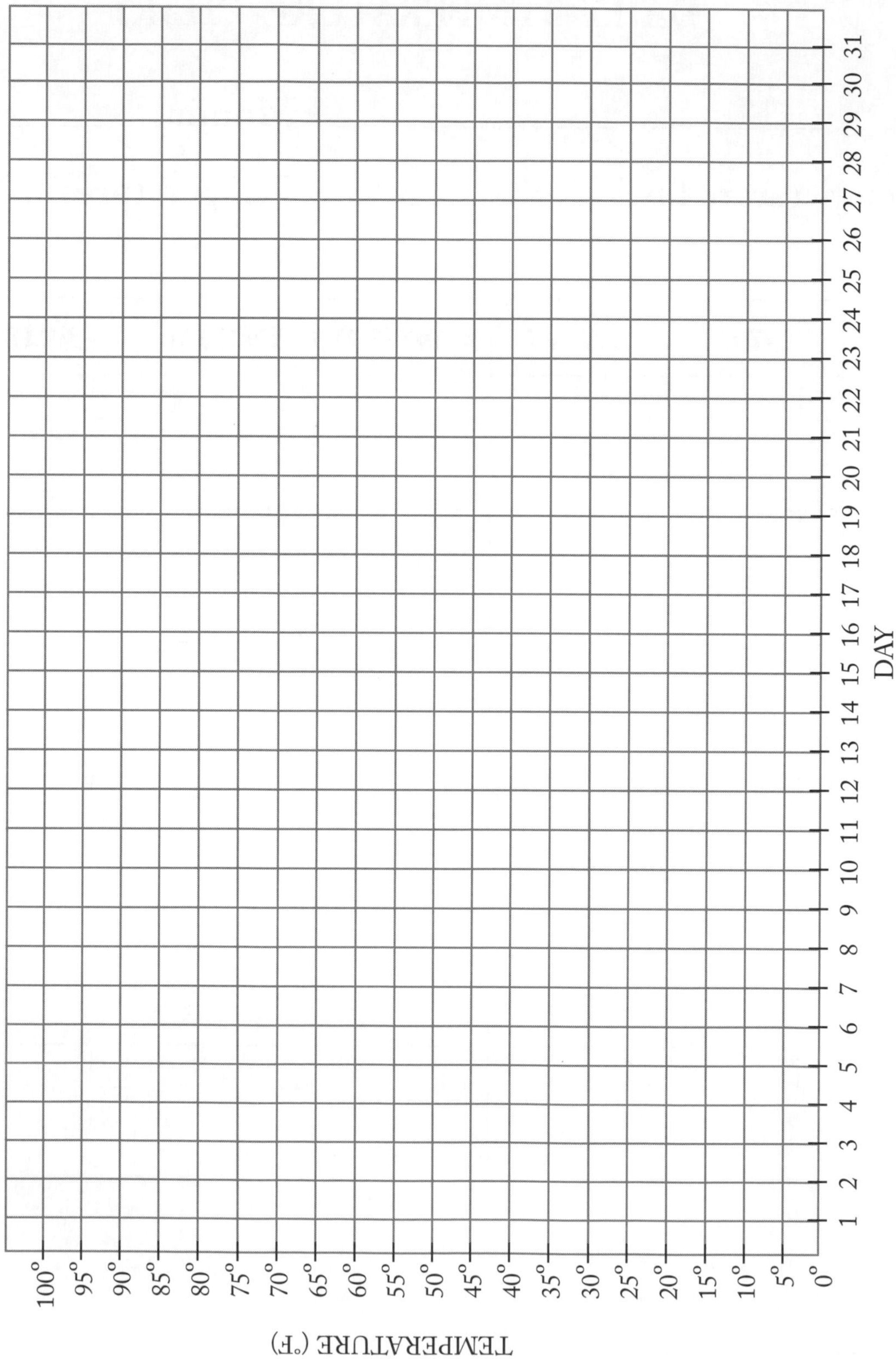

DAY

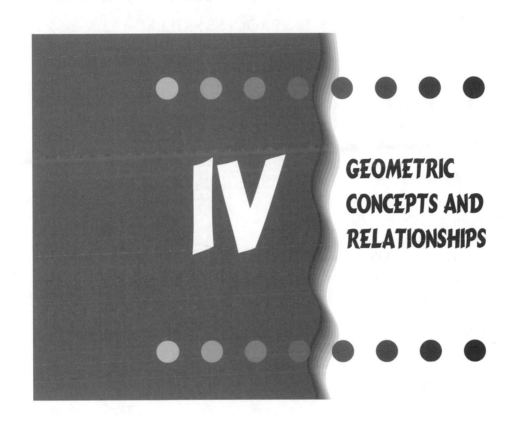

IV

GEOMETRIC CONCEPTS AND RELATIONSHIPS

NAMES AND SHAPES

PRIMARY CONTENT

Recognizing two-dimensional geometric shapes

PRIOR STUDENT KNOWLEDGE

Prior exposure to geometric shapes and their written names

PRE-ACTIVITY PREPARATION

Using 4 in. x 6 in. index cards, make a deck of thirty-two geometric cards. Make one deck for each group. On sixteen cards, write the names of the four basic shapes as follows: Write *circle* on four cards, *triangle* on four cards, *square* on four cards, and *rectangle* on four cards. On the remaining sixteen cards, draw pictures of the four basic shapes as follows: Draw a circle on four cards, a triangle on four cards, a square on four cards, and a rectangle on four cards. Make the shapes decreasing in size, and vary the type (if applicable). Lastly, number the shape cards. Number the largest shape 4 and the smallest shape 1. Examples of the sixteen shape cards are illustrated in step 1 of the Procedure. Separate the sixteen name cards from the sixteen picture cards, securing each sub-deck with a rubber band. Cards may be laminated, if desired, for durability.

PROCESS SKILLS

Observing, comparing, sorting, matching, calculating

GROUP SIZE

3–4 students

MATERIALS PER GROUP

1 deck of 32 geometric cards

TEACHER INFORMATION

Names and Shapes is an activity that progresses rather quickly, and several games can be played in a short period of time.

100

Mathematics Activities (KSAM)

PROCEDURE

1. Distribute a deck of geometric cards (separated into the two sub-decks of name cards and picture cards) to each group. One example of what the sixteen picture cards might look like is shown below.

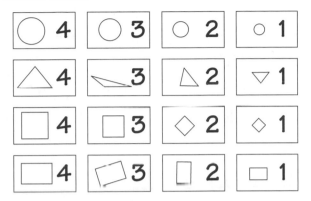

2. In each group, one student shuffles the word cards and another student shuffles the picture cards.

3. Each shuffled sub-deck is placed facedown in the middle of the playing surface, resulting in two stacks of cards.

4. The first player draws one card from each stack—one word card and one picture card.

5. If a matching pair is drawn—the word card names the picture—the player places the matching pair faceup on the table and orally states the name. If the player draws two cards that do not match, those cards are held by the player.

6. Play continues in a clockwise direction, one draw from each stack per turn. If drawn cards do not match, but make one or more matches with held cards, then those matching pairs may be laid down.

7. The game continues until all the cards in the two piles have been drawn.

8. Each player then adds up the numbers on the shape cards in his/her matching pairs.

9. The player with the highest total is the winner.

10. At the end of play, students sort the cards into the two sub-decks and secure with rubber bands.

EXTENSIONS AND ADAPTATIONS

1. All the cards could be placed facedown on a table or floor to play a memory game (for example, Concentration).

2. An odd card may be added to the deck to play a card game similar to Old Maid.

3. The students may subtract the total points remaining in their hands at the end of the game from the total points in their matching cards.

4. This activity is appropriate for use in a learning center.

5. Related activities Shape Patterns on page 102 and Everything's in Shape on page 108.

SHAPE PATTERNS

PRIMARY CONTENT
Synthesizing, creating, and repeating shape patterns using the four basic geometric shapes

PRIOR STUDENT KNOWLEDGE
Recognition of basic shapes (circle, square, rectangle, and triangle)

PRE-ACTIVITY PREPARATION
If attribute blocks are not available, cut out the four basic shapes (circle, square, rectangle, and triangle) from construction paper. Make enough shapes to provide five or six of each shape to each group. For a given shape, the size and color should be identical.

PROCESS SKILLS
Observing, comparing, classifying, matching

GROUP SIZE
2 students

MATERIALS PER GROUP
Attribute blocks or construction-paper shapes (circles, squares, rectangles, triangles), approximately 5 or 6 of each shape

TEACHER INFORMATION
No special teacher information is required.

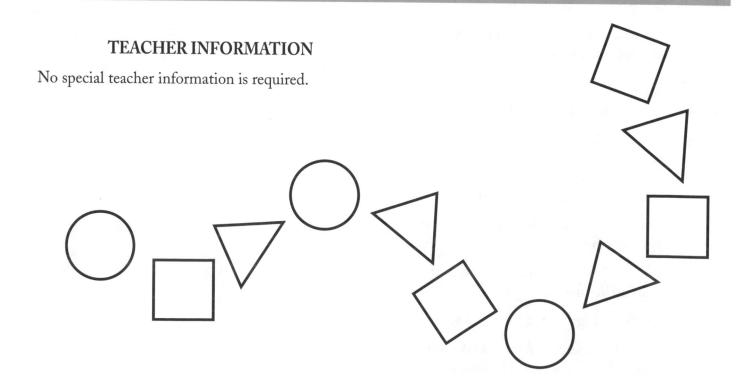

PROCEDURE

1. Conduct a brief review of the four basic shapes and their names. Include drawings on the board.

2. Divide the class into pairs and distribute materials. Depending on the size of the shapes, student pairs may work at a desk or on the floor.

3. Demonstrate the three steps in the activity:

Step A: While one student's back is turned, the second student arranges selected shapes, in a line, in a repeating pattern. The pattern may contain any or all of the four basic shapes (not all the shapes need to be used); the pattern may contain multiples of a given shape; and the pattern must be repeated at least twice (can be more) in the line. Two examples are shown below, one with a simple pattern and one with a more complex pattern.

△□○△□○△□○△□○
□△○○□□△□△○○□□△

Step B: When the pattern line has been completed, the first student turns around and attempts to identify the shape pattern. Specifically, the student should write the progression of shape names demonstrated by the pattern (identified in either left-to-right progression or right-to-left progression) and the number of times the pattern was repeated in the line. Using the two examples in the previous step, the correct responses would be (in left-to-right progression):

△□○|△□○|△□○|△□○

triangle, square, circle—4 times
(4 repetitions)

□△○○□□△|□△○○□□△

rectangle, triangle, circle, circle, square, rectangle, triangle—2 times

Step C: Students then reverse roles and repeat the process.

4. Once the activity has been demonstrated, allow student pairs to complete the activity on their own. Allow enough time so that each student gets at least three or four turns. Encourage students not to make every pattern as complex as they can. Encourage students to vary their patterns from relatively simple to relatively complex.

EXTENSIONS AND ADAPTATIONS

1. Have students complete this activity using basic shapes created from clay.

2. This activity is appropriate for use in a learning center.

3. Related activities Names and Shapes on page 100 and Everything's in Shape on page 108.

PICK YOUR MIND

PRIMARY CONTENT

Geometrical comprehension

PRIOR STUDENT KNOWLEDGE

Familiarity with basic shapes

PRE-ACTIVITY PREPARATION

Copy reproducible Student Data Sheet (page 107), one copy per student.

PROCESS SKILLS

Observing, counting, recording, predicting, problem solving

GROUP SIZE

Individual

MATERIALS PER GROUP

- 50 flat toothpicks
- 1 copy of reproducible Student Data Sheet

TEACHER INFORMATION

No special teacher information is required.

PROCEDURE

1. Distribute toothpicks and a Student Data Sheet to each student.

2. Ask students to make a square using one toothpick per side. Discuss how many toothpicks were needed to make the square. Lead students to see that if they had made sixteen separate squares of that size, sixty-four toothpicks (4 x 16) would have been used. Now ask, "I wonder if there is a way to make sixteen equal-sized squares with less than sixty-four toothpicks?"

3. Challenge students to attempt that task—to make sixteen equal-sized squares using as few toothpicks as possible. Tell students that they get three attempts (allow more if desired). After each attempt, they should each record on their Student Data Sheet the actual number of toothpicks used, along with a drawing that shows their sixteen squares for that attempt.

4. Conduct a class discussion at the conclusion of the activity during which Student Data Sheets may be compared and/or displayed. During the discussion, indicate that there are many ways to combine the toothpicks to get sixteen squares. A few examples are shown below.

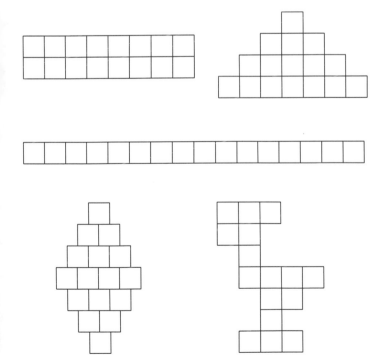

Lead students to understand, however, that the best way (most efficient use of toothpicks) is to combine the squares into a square formation since this shape maximizes the internal sharing of toothpicks (sides) by adjacent squares. As shown below, this approach requires only forty toothpicks for the sixteen squares.

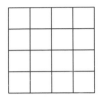

EXTENSIONS AND ADAPTATIONS

1. This activity is appropriate for use in a learning center.

2. Different shapes (triangles or rectangles) may be substituted for squares in this activity.

3. Several puzzles can be made with toothpicks. Some examples are:

   a) Take away one toothpick and leave three equal squares.

   b) Take away eight toothpicks and leave three squares.

   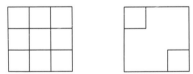

PICK YOUR MIND _____

STUDENT DATA SHEET

Name_____

	Number of Toothpicks	Number of Squares	Drawing
1.		16	
2.		16	
3.		16	

EVERYTHING'S IN SHAPE _____

PRIMARY CONTENT
- Identifying and working with the four basic shapes (circle, square, rectangle, triangle)
- Constructing a simple bar graph

PRIOR STUDENT KNOWLEDGE
Previous exposure to basic two-dimensional geometric shapes

PRE-ACTIVITY PREPARATION
Copy reproducible Shape Graph (page 110), one copy per student.

PROCESS SKILLS
Observing, comparing, classifying, counting, graphing

GROUP SIZE
Individual

MATERIALS PER GROUP
- 1 large sheet of drawing paper
- Several sheets of construction paper of various colors
- 1 pair of scissors
- Glue
- 1 straightedge
- Crayons
- 1 copy of reproducible Shape Graph

TEACHER INFORMATION
No special teacher information is required.

PROCEDURE

1. Conduct a brief review of the four basic shapes and their names. Include an ample number of drawings on the board illustrating the great diversity the four shapes can take as their dimensions are varied. Also discuss how frequently variations of these four shapes appear in our everyday world. Lead students to see that, in fact, most of what we see can be reduced to variations of these four shapes. For example, the sun is a circle; trees are circles atop long, extended rectangles; houses are squares or rectangles with triangles on top; the ears of animals are triangles, their heads are circles, their bodies are rectangles, and their legs can be pictured as long, skinny rectangles; and so on.

2. Distribute to each student all the materials except the reproducible.

3. Challenge students to create a scene on their drawing paper. The scene can be of anything they want and can include anything they want. The only restriction is that the scene and its contents must be constructed of variations of circles, squares, rectangles, and triangles cut from the construction paper and glued to the drawing paper. Crayons may be used for additional color, and pencil and/or crayon may be used to add in detail. Encourage them to use their imaginations and to use combinations of shapes to get unusual effects.

4. When the pictures have been completed, have each student add a title and his/her name.

5. Distribute the reproducible Shape Graph to each student.

6. Tell students to color in one box for each time they used a circle on their picture, beginning with the bottom box, then working upward.

7. Students should repeat step 6 with the square, rectangle, and triangle.

8. Take time to let students share their pictures with the class. Give special praise to those students who used the shapes imaginatively. Also discuss the results of the graphing activity. Include questions such as:

   * Which shape did you use the most? The least?
   * Did everyone use the same number of circles?
   * Who used the most triangles?

9. Display students' pictures in the room or hallway.

EXTENSIONS AND ADAPTATIONS

1. Have students create a picture using only circles, only triangles, etc.

2. This activity is appropriate for use in a learning center.

3. Related geometric-shape activities Names and Shapes on page 100 and Shape Patterns on page 102.

4. Related graphing activity A Hairy Graph on page 116.

EVERYTHING'S IN SHAPE

SHAPE GRAPH

Name_____

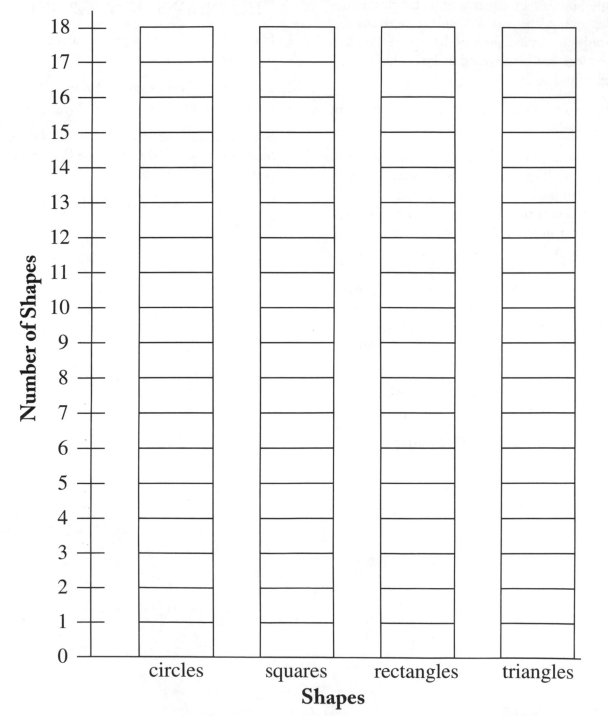

© Curriculum Associates, Inc.   *Mathematics Activities (KSAM)*

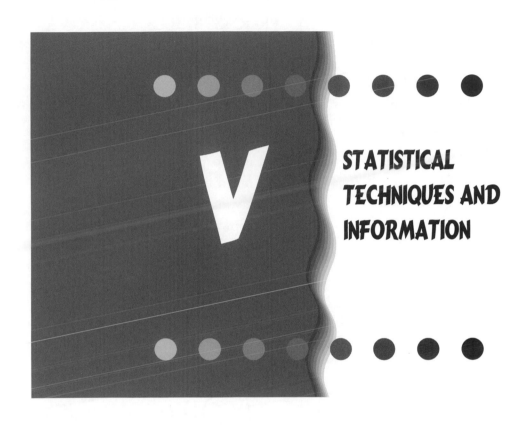

V

STATISTICAL TECHNIQUES AND INFORMATION

DOTS OR WHAT? _____

PRIMARY CONTENT
Number patterns

PROCESS SKILLS
Observing

PRIOR STUDENT KNOWLEDGE
No special prior knowledge is required.

GROUP SIZE
2–5 students

PRE-ACTIVITY PREPARATION
1. Collect newspaper pictures, enough for one picture per group.
2. Copy reproducibles Coded Picture 1 (page 114) and Coded Picture 2 (page 115), one copy of each per student.

MATERIALS PER GROUP
• 1 newspaper picture
• 1 magnifying glass
• Crayons
• 1 copy of reproducible Coded Picture 1 for each student
• 1 copy of reproducible Coded Picture 2 for each student

TEACHER INFORMATION

No special teacher information is required.

PROCEDURE

1. Introduce the activity by telling students that mathematics can even be used to form pictures through what is called numerical coding. (Coding is also the underlying principle in the complex process of picture transmission over a telephone wire—a fax—or through the air—a TV picture.) This is done by number coding various shades and/or colors and using points (dots) to make a picture. Perhaps the best example of picture coding is a newspaper picture.

2. Group students and distribute a newspaper picture and magnifying glass to each group. Have students examine the picture closely under magnification. Lead them to see that the picture is really a composite of many tiny black dots (for a black and white picture) and that the darker areas of the picture are where the black dots are closer together, while the lighter areas are where the dots are more widely spaced apart. If the picture is in color, the same basic principle applies using dots of various colors.

3. Ask students if they can think of other possible examples of picture coding (TV pictures, paint-by-number pictures, pictures or text on a computer monitor, etc.).

4. Now distribute reproducible Coded Picture 1 and crayons to each student for individual work. Tell students that there is a picture hidden there and that they will have to do some "decoding" work before it can be seen. The code they should use is: 1 = yellow, 2 = tan, 3 = medium brown, 4 = black, and 5 = pink. Students should color the squares accordingly and see if they can identify the picture. (It is a teddy bear, but don't let the secret out!) Also tell students that similar to a newspaper picture that is viewed too closely or under magnification (the eye concentrates on the individual dots and not the whole composite), the picture may be hard to identify if it is viewed close up. For best results, it should be viewed from a distance of roughly ten to twenty feet.

5. When students think they have identified the picture, they should NOT tell their classmates. Rather, they should each raise their hand and confirm their identification quietly with you.

6. After the picture has been correctly identified, distribute reproducible Coded Picture 2 to each student. Repeat step 4 for class work, or you may let students take the picture home for decoding. The code for picture 2 is: 0 = white or off-white, 1 = medium gray, and 10 = black. Proper decoding of picture 2 should reveal Abraham Lincoln (when viewed from a distance).

EXTENSIONS AND ADAPTATIONS

1. This activity is appropriate for use in a learning center.

2. Distribute another copy of Coded Picture 1 to each student. Let students develop and use their own color code. The same can be done for Coded Picture 2.

3. Let students devise their own code sheet for a picture.

DOTS OR WHAT?

CODED PICTURE 1

Name_____

Directions: Color "1" yellow, color "2" tan, color "3" medium brown, color "4" black, and color "5" pink.

1	1	1	1	1	1	1	1	1	1	1	1	1
1	1	1	1	1	3	3	3	3	1	2	2	1
1	1	2	2	3	3	3	3	3	3	2	2	2
1	2	2	3	3	3	3	3	3	3	2	2	2
1	1	2	3	5	3	3	5	3	3	2	2	1
1	1	1	3	2	4	2	3	3	3	1	1	1
1	1	1	3	2	2	2	3	3	3	1	1	1
1	1	1	1	2	2	3	3	3	3	1	1	1
1	4	4	3	3	3	3	3	3	3	4	4	4
1	4	3	3	3	3	3	3	3	3	4	4	2
1	1	3	3	3	3	3	3	3	3	4	4	4
1	4	4	4	3	3	3	3	3	3	1	1	1
2	2	4	4	1	1	4	4	4	4	1	1	1
1	2	4	1	1	1	1	4	4	2	1	1	1
1	1	1	1	1	1	1	4	2	2	1	1	1
1	1	1	1	1	1	1	1	1	1	1	1	1

DOTS OR WHAT?

CODED PICTURE 2

Name_____

Directions: Color "0" white or off-white, color "1" medium gray, and color "10" black.

0	0	0	0	0	0	1	10	10	1	0	0	0	0
0	0	0	0	0	1	10	10	10	10	1	0	0	0
0	0	0	1	10	10	0	1	10	10	10	1	0	0
0	0	0	10	10	1	0	0	0	1	10	10	0	0
0	0	0	10	1	1	1	0	0	0	10	10	1	0
0	0	10	10	1	0	0	1	1	1	0	1	10	0
0	0	10	1	10	1	0	10	10	1	10	10	10	0
0	0	10	0	10	1	1	10	10	0	10	10	0	0
0	0	10	0	1	1	0	0	1	10	1	10	0	0
0	0	0	10	1	10	1	0	1	0	1	10	0	0
0	0	0	10	10	10	0	1	0	1	10	10	0	0
0	0	0	0	10	10	1	0	0	1	10	1	0	0
0	0	0	1	10	10	1	10	10	10	10	1	0	0
0	0	0	1	10	0	10	10	10	10	10	1	0	0
0	1	10	10	10	10	0	1	1	0	10	0	0	0
10	10	10	1	1	1	10	10	10	1	1	10	1	0
10	10	1	1	1	10	10	10	10	10	10	10	10	1
10	1	1	10	10	10	10	10	10	1	1	10	10	10

A HAIRY GRAPH

PRIMARY CONTENT
- Gathering data
- Constructing and interpreting a pictograph

PRIOR STUDENT KNOWLEDGE
No special prior knowledge is required.

PRE-ACTIVITY PREPARATION
1. On a standard sheet (22 in. x 28 in.) of poster board, draw a pictograph, using the illustration shown in step 3 of the Procedure as a guide. Label the graph OUR HAIRY CLASS GRAPH. The graph should have four columns (bars) labeled: Red, Brown, Black, Blonde. Each column should be 3 in. wide. It is recommended that column lines be lightly penciled in to aid students in positioning their cards. Each hair-color card is 2 in. high. Thus, if 2 in. of space is allowed at the top and the bottom of the graph for labeling, a sheet of poster board should accommodate a maximum of twelve entries for any given hair color. If there will be more than twelve entries for a given color, the height of the graph can be increased by taping on an additional section of poster board.
2. Copy reproducible supplement Hair-Color Cards (page 119) and cut out the cards. Make enough so that each student has one card.

PROCESS SKILLS
Comparing, classifying, gathering, recording, graphing, interpreting

GROUP SIZE
Whole class followed by groups of 3–5 students

MATERIALS PER GROUP
- Poster-board graph (for whole class)
- 1 hair-color card for each student
- Crayons (1 each of red, brown, black, and yellow) for each student
- Glue or tape (for whole class)

TEACHER INFORMATION
No special teacher information is required.

PROCEDURE

1. Ask students to name the four basic hair colors (red, brown, black, and blonde). Write those colors on the board. Survey students to see how hair color is distributed within the class, writing the number of students with each color below that color name on the board. (Avoid tones and shades of colors—require that students select the basic color that they think most closely matches their hair.)

2. Inquire if there is another way, perhaps a better way, to present the hair-color information presently listed on the board. Lead students to the idea of presentation in the form of a bar graph or pictograph.

3. Distribute the materials and show students the prepared poster-board graph. Place the graph where it is easily accessible by all students. An example of the graph is illustrated below.

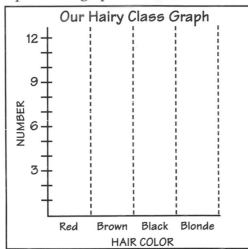

4. Each student draws a picture of himself/herself on the hair-color card. Ask that they pay special attention to their hair, perhaps even overemphasizing the hair relative to the rest of the picture. After the hair is outlined, students color the hair with one of the four basic colors—the one that is the closest match. The student's first name should then be written vertically downward in the left box on the card, while the right box should contain the student's hair color, also written vertically downward.

5. As the cards are completed, have each student come forward and glue or tape his/her card in the appropriate column on the class graph.

6. When the graph has been completed, conduct a class discussion of results, including questions such as:

   • What is the most common hair color in our class?

   • What is the least common hair color in our class?

   • Would this be true of all classes (groups of students)? Why or why not?

   • What are the advantages of showing data in graph form rather than just number form?

During the discussion, explain that graphs (in this case a pictograph) help us compare sets by showing which sets are largest and which are smallest in number and that it is easier to count and compare sets when they are in visual columns.

7. Divide the class into groups of 3–5 students.

8. Each group will decide its own topic to survey (for example, shoe size, student sensitivity, favorite color, favorite food, favorite TV show, birthday month, etc.). In addition, each group will:

   a. Survey other students in the class and tally the results.

   b. Create a bar graph from their results, including numbered and/or labeled axes.

   c. Decide on a graph-related question to ask the other students.

   d. Compare and discuss the graphs in a class discussion.

EXTENSIONS AND ADAPTATIONS

1. Have students collect data from a larger population, such as family members or students in other classes.

2. Students might find examples of bar graphs in the newspaper and report on them.

3. Related activities Record a Temp on page 94 and Everything's in Shape on page 108.

A HAIRY GRAPH

HAIR-COLOR CARDS

Mathematics Activities (KSAM)

GRID IT OUT _____

PRIMARY CONTENT
Locating points on a grid

PRIOR STUDENT KNOWLEDGE
No special prior knowledge is required.

PRE-ACTIVITY PREPARATION
1. Make an overhead transparency of a grid for use during class discussion, using Overhead Transparency Grid (page 122). Or, if preferred, use page 122 as a guide and draw a large grid on the board.
2. Copy reproducibles Find Me Grid Sheet (page 123) and Make a Picture Grid Sheet (page 124), one copy of each per student.

PROCESS SKILLS
Observing, recording, interpreting

GROUP SIZE
Whole class

MATERIALS PER GROUP
- 1 Overhead Transparency Grid OR grid drawn on board
- Overhead projector
- Crayons for each student
- 1 copy of reproducible Find Me Grid Sheet for each student
- 1 copy of reproducible Make a Picture Grid Sheet for each student

TEACHER INFORMATION

Procedures for locating points on a grid that must be stressed are as follows.

1. Always begin in the lower left corner (0, 0).

2. Move to the right horizontally according to the first number.

3. Move up vertically according to the second number.

4. The point at which two lines intersect is named by two numbers; the first being the horizontal number, and the second being the vertical number.

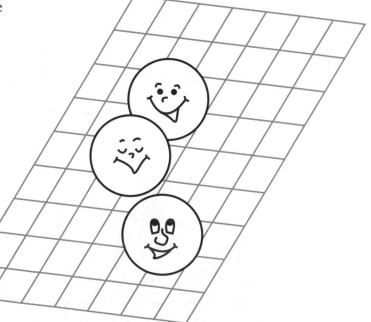

PROCEDURE

1. Place a smiley face at some line-intersection point on the Overhead Transparency Grid (or a grid drawn on the board), and place a small stick man at the (0, 0) point. To introduce the activity, prompt students with the question, "Mr. Stick Man would like to visit Mr. Smiley, but he doesn't know where he lives (doesn't know his address); what would be the best way to explain to Mr. Stick Man where Mr. Smiley is located (Mr. Smiley's address)?" Help students see that grid coordinates give exact locations and that to use coordinates in this example they should:

   a. always start at the lower-left corner;

   b. move to the right horizontally (across) to under the smiley face and write down the number they see; and

   c. move up to the smiley face and check to find what number is to the left of the smiley face.

   Stress that they must move along the lines, and the point at which two lines intersect is named by two numbers. In both cases, the horizontal coordinate is always given first, and the vertical coordinate is always given second. (The Overhead Transparency Grid is set up to use either method.)

2. Allow a student to write the grid location of Mr. Smiley on the board.

3. Now move the smiley face to another line-intersection point and have students determine where the smiley face is located. (Caution students to write the horizontal number first, then a comma, and then the vertical number.) Repeat the procedure as often as needed to insure understanding.

4. Give the location (coordinates) of a hidden smiley face and ask a student to find the location of the face and plot it. Repeat as often as desired.

5. Distribute crayons and the Find Me Grid Sheet to each student and complete it as a class. Allow students to color their completed grid picture. (See Answer Key, page 154.)

6. Distribute the Make a Picture Grid Sheet (a little more difficult!) to each student. They should complete and color this grid picture individually. (See Answer Key, page 154.)

EXTENSIONS AND ADAPTATIONS

1. This activity is appropriate for use in a learning center.

2. Have students complete the reproducible Secret Words Grid Sheet on page 125. (See Answer Key, page 154.)

GRID IT OUT_____

OVERHEAD TRANSPARENCY GRID

Name_____

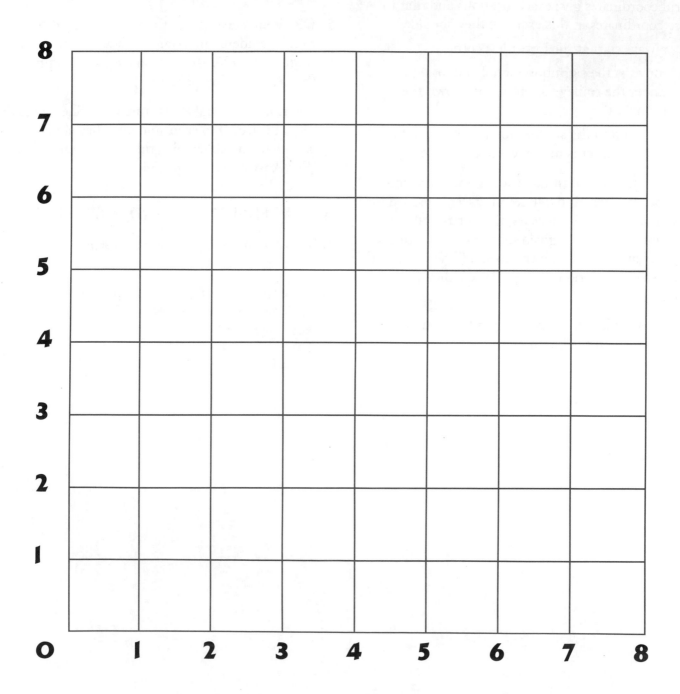

© Curriculum Associates, Inc.   *Mathematics Activities (KSAM)*

GRID IT OUT

FIND ME GRID SHEET

Name_____

Directions: Locate point 1 and make a dot on the grid. Locate point 2 and make another dot. Connect the two dots. Locate point 3 and connect the dot at point 2 to point 3. Continue in a dot-to-dot pattern.

point 1 = (5, 3)
point 2 = (0, 3)
point 3 = (1, 2)
point 4 = (7, 2)
point 5 = (8, 3)
point 6 = (5, 3)
point 7 = (5, 8)
point 8 = (1, 4)
point 9 = (5, 4)

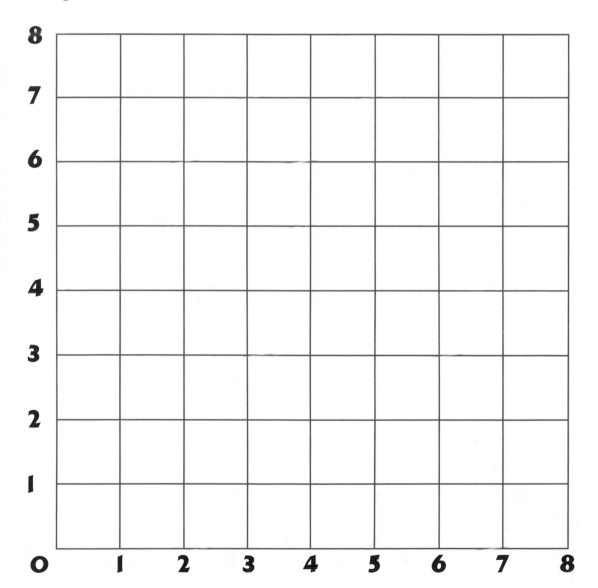

Mathematics Activities (KSAM)

GRID IT OUT _____

MAKE A PICTURE GRID SHEET

Name_____

Directions: Find each of these points on the grid. Make a dot in the correct place, and label it with the correct letter. Connect the dots in alphabetical order.

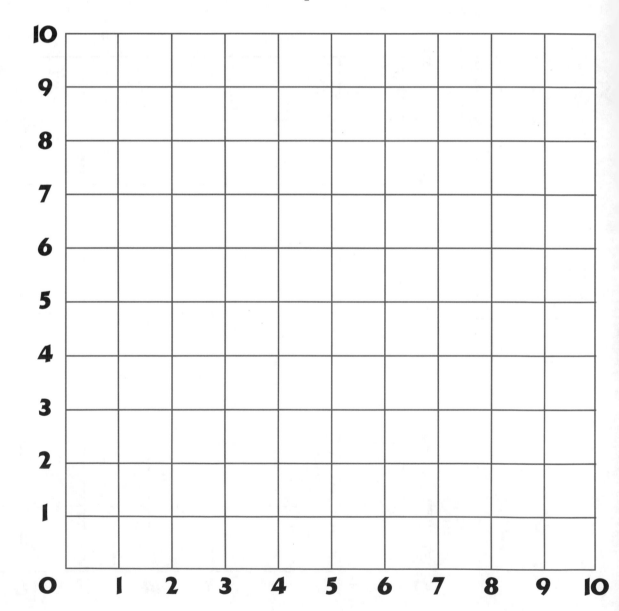

A (6, 0)
B (5, 1)
C (3, 1)
D (2, 0)
E (1, 1)
F (3, 3)
G (5, 3)
H (5, 8)
I (4, 10)
J (3, 8)
K (3, 1)
L (5, 1)
M (5, 3)
N (7, 1)
O (6, 0)
P (8, 0)
Q (8, 6)
R (4, 6)
S (8, 7)
T (9, 7)
U (9, 0)
V (10, 0)

GRID IT OUT

SECRET WORDS GRID SHEET

Name

Directions: Find the letter that matches the grid pair (coordinates) to find the words below.

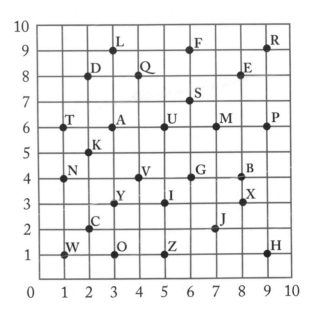

Example: 1. (1, 1) (9, 1) (5, 3) (5, 1)   (2, 5) (5, 3) (2, 8)
          W   H   I   Z   K   I   D

2. (9, 1) (5, 6) (7, 6) (3, 6) (1, 4)

3. (9, 9) (3, 6) (5, 3) (1, 4) (8, 4) (3, 1) (1, 1)

4. (6, 7) (3, 1) (2, 8) (3, 6)   (9, 6) (3, 1) (9, 6)

5. (4, 4) (3, 1) (3, 9) (2, 2) (3, 6) (1, 4) (3, 1)

MAIL DELIVERY

PRIMARY CONTENT
Locating points on a grid

PRIOR STUDENT KNOWLEDGE
At least some previous exposure to grids and grid coordinates

PRE-ACTIVITY PREPARATION
1. Arrange students' desks so that they are in horizontal and vertical rows, forming a grid.
2. Determine each student's coordinates (desk position) on the grid. Using 3 in. x 5 in. index cards, make a grid card for each student. For example, a student's desk coordinates might be (4, 5). Also lightly write the student's name in a corner of the card on the same side as the coordinates to facilitate distribution.
3. Prepare a "letter" for each student, addressed only with the student's grid coordinates (no names). The letters can range from simple messages on index cards to actual envelopes containing notes. The letters can be made to be fun and exciting for the students.

PROCESS SKILLS
Observing, comparing, matching, interpreting

GROUP SIZE
Whole class

MATERIALS PER GROUP
- 1 grid card for each student
- 1 letter addressed (by grid coordinates) to each student, stacked in a classroom post office

TEACHER INFORMATION

In order to locate points on a grid, the students should be reminded to:

1. always begin in the lower-left corner;

2. move to the right horizontally according to the first number;

3. move up vertically according to the second number.

PROCEDURE

1. Distribute the appropriate grid card to each student, locating their placement on the grid. The grid cards should be placed facedown (coordinates down) on the students' desks.

2. For practice, select a few students, one at a time, to stand up—thus demonstrating their grid points to the class. Refer to these grid points as their addresses.

3. After choosing one student to be the Mail Carrier, name an address. For example, name (5, 3).

4. The mail carrier will decide, using grid-point location skills, who lives at (5, 3); will sort through the mail for the letter belonging to (5, 3); and will then deliver the letter, checking (turning over) the address card on the recipient's desk to see if a correct delivery has been made. If an error has been made, the Mail Carrier redelivers the letter (with assistance if necessary).

5. The student to whom the letter has been correctly delivered now becomes the Mail Carrier, and the process is repeated.

6. The activity continues until all the letters have been delivered.

EXTENSIONS AND ADAPTATIONS

1. Class Grid Alphabet Letters: Arrange students' desks to form a grid as in the activity procedure. Grid cards are again distributed as in step 1. In addition, each student is given a copy of the reproducible Class Grid Alphabet Letters. (See page 129.) Call out several grid points which will make, when combined, a letter of the alphabet. (See example on the supplement Class Grid Alphabet Letters Example on page 128.) The students at these points will stand up, while the remainder of the class plots the grid points on their grid sheets. This allows students who are seated to guess what letter the grid combination has formed—either by the pattern on their grid sheet or by observing the students standing.

2. Using the reproducible Class Grid Alphabet Letters, let students design a letter or number of their choice through grid coordinates. Then let them exchange coordinate lists and attempt to decipher the letters or numbers.

3. Related activity Grid It Out on page 120.

MAIL DELIVERY

CLASS GRID ALPHABET LETTERS EXAMPLE
(EXAMPLE SHOWN IS "H")

Name_____

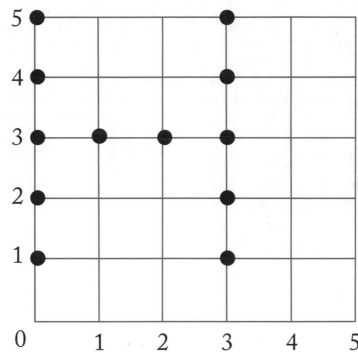

I	O	P	H	L
(1, 0)	(1, 4)	(5, 5)	(0, 5)	(2, 5)
(2, 0)	(1, 3)	(4, 5)	(0, 4)	(2, 4)
(3, 0)	(1, 2)	(3, 5)	(0, 3)	(2, 3)
(2, 1)	(2, 2)	(3, 4)	(0, 2)	(2, 2)
(2, 2)	(3, 2)	(3, 3)	(0, 1)	(2, 1)
(2, 3)	(3, 3)	(4, 3)	(1, 3)	(2, 0)
(1, 3)	(3, 4)	(5, 3)	(2, 3)	(3, 0)
(3, 3)	(2, 4)	(5, 4)	(3, 3)	(4, 0)
		(3, 2)	(3, 4)	(5, 0)
		(3, 1)	(3, 5)	
		(3, 0)	(3, 2)	
			(3, 1)	

MAIL DELIVERY

CLASS GRID ALPHABET LETTERS

Name

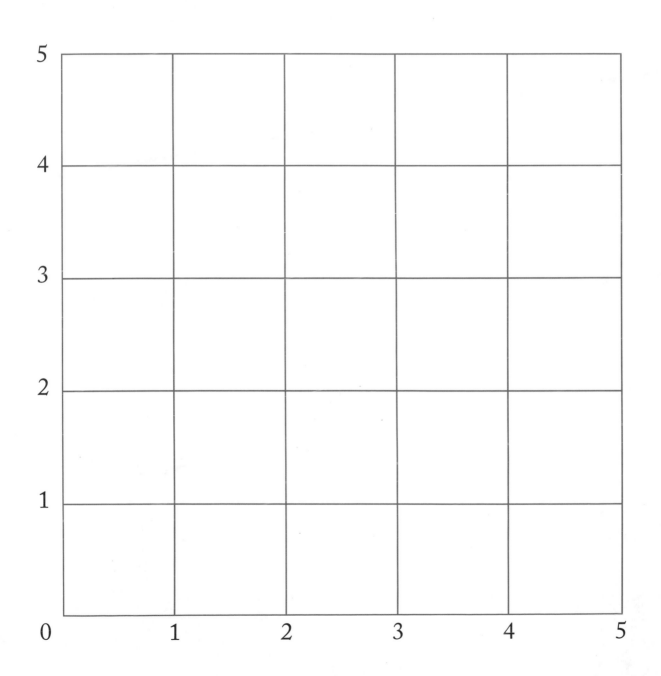

VI

PROBLEM-
SOLVING
STRATEGIES

ARITHME"TIC TAC TOE"

PRIMARY CONTENT

Solving two-step word problems using basic skills

PRIOR STUDENT KNOWLEDGE

Experience in the operations of addition, subtraction, and basic multiplication

PRE-ACTIVITY PREPARATION

Copy reproducibles Tic Tac Toe 1 (page 134) and Tic Tac Toe 2 (page 135), one copy of each per student.

PROCESS SKILLS

Calculating, interpreting, problem solving

GROUP SIZE

Individual

MATERIALS PER GROUP

- 1 copy of reproducible Tic Tac Toe 1
- 1 copy of reproducible Tic Tac Toe 2

TEACHER INFORMATION

No special teacher information is required.

PROCEDURE

1. Distribute one copy of reproducible Tic Tac Toe 1 to each student.

2. Direct students to randomly fill in the tic-tac-toe board with numbers in the box. (They will use only nine of the eleven numbers in the box; two of the eleven are bogus answers.)

3. Students may choose any numbered problem on the page, solve it, and mark (X) the answer on the tic-tac-toe board. (See Answer Key, page 154.)

4. Students are to work enough problems to get two tic-tac-toes (three Xs in two lines). (Note: even if a student happens to place both bogus numbers on the board, there will still be three possible tic-tac-toes.)

5. Give each student a copy of reproducible Tic Tac Toe 2. This time students are to devise nine problems of their own with answers matching numbers in the number box. (Again, two of the eleven numbers will be bogus answers.) Stress that it is especially good—but not mandatory—if problems include at least two of the three operations (addition, subtraction, and multiplication). When students have finished, ask them to exchange papers and solve/check each other's problems as in steps 2–4.

EXTENSIONS AND ADAPTATIONS

1. Have pairs of students use reproducible Tic Tac Toe 1 and take turns solving problems until one student gets a tic-tac-toe.

2. A suitable set of problems involving fractions and mixed numbers can be developed.

3. This activity is appropriate for use in a learning center.

4. Related activity Operation on page 136.

ARITHME"TIC TAC TOE"

TIC TAC TOE 1

Name_____

Directions: Choose any problem below and solve it. Put an X on the board over the correct number. You win with 3 Xs in a row!

PROBLEMS:

1. I had 45 baseball cards. I gave 25 of them to my friend. My friend gave me 18 of his cards. How many cards do I have now?

2. How many total legs are there on 8 pigs, 4 cows, and 6 chickens?

3. There are 3 teams of second graders and 6 teams of third graders. Each team has 9 players. How many players are there?

4. In her basket, Lena had 7 apples, 11 oranges, 5 bananas, and 13 pears. During the day she sold 34 pieces of fruit. How many pieces of fruit are left?

5. I had $20. I spent $3.50, $3.75, and $6.75. How many dollars do I have left?

6. Mario worked every day for 3 weeks. Jake worked for 17 days. How many more days did Mario work than Jake?

7. I bought 4 items for $5.75, $5.50, $4.50, and $1.25. I gave the clerk $20. How much change will I get back in dollars?

8. Teresa had 175 marbles. She gave 43 marbles to Kai, 21 marbles to Julio, 19 marbles to Carl, and 15 marbles to Sara. How many marbles will Teresa have to give to Meghan so that Teresa ends up without any marbles?

9. If I went up 21 floors in an elevator, down 1 floor, up 6 floors, and down 2 floors, how many floors up am I from my starting point?

Fill in the spaces with any of these numbers.

108	2		9
38	81	60	6
4	24	3	77

Mathematics Activities (KSAM)

ARITHME"TIC TAC TOE" _____._____

TIC TAC TOE 2

Name_____

Now, it's your turn.

108	2		9
38	81	60	6
4	24	3	77

1. _____

2. _____

3. _____

4. _____

5. _____

6. _____

7. _____

8. _____

9. _____

OPERATION _____

PRIMARY CONTENT

- Solving one-step and/or two-step word problems
- Techniques for problem solving

PRIOR STUDENT KNOWLEDGE

No special prior knowledge is required.

PRE-ACTIVITY PREPARATION

1. Compile a set of at least four one-step and/or two-step word problems appropriate for the grade level. Write the problems on an overhead transparency so that only one problem at a time can be revealed. Or, if desired, problems can be written on the board and covered.
2. (Optional) Gather various hospital props such as a white lab coat, face mask, rubber gloves, hair net, etc. for use by you and/or students.

PROCESS SKILLS

Observing, calculating, problem solving

GROUP SIZE

Whole class

MATERIALS PER GROUP

- At least four word problems on an overhead transparency or written on the board
- (Optional) Various hospital props (see Pre-Activity Preparation)

TEACHER INFORMATION

This activity uses the following four basic steps for problem solving: read, plan, solve, check. Students often resist checking their answers. It can be stressed that most doctors would not perform an operation and never check on their patient. The similarities to a medical operation can be used and extended, including statements such as: "Dr. Fran (student), what is your diagnosis?" and "Review panel, do you agree with the doctor's decision to operate?" If desired, you and/or students can wear some medical attire to help set the mood.

PROCEDURE

1. In this activity, the classroom becomes a hospital operating room, with the doctor preparing and then completing surgery. You are the head doctor with a complete staff of assistants (the class). The class may be divided into four groups of surgeons, each group to complete one phase of the "operation." The other groups observe as each phase is completed.

    a. Examine the patient's chart (read the revealed problem). This group is responsible for knowing all the details before the operation. They should discuss, so all can hear, the important information for the operation.

    b. Plan the operation (decide on the mathematical operations to be used). This group decides whether addition or subtraction or multiplication will be used. In more complicated problems, two or more operations may be used. This group must decide the order if more than one is to be used.

    c. Complete the operation (solve the problem). This group does the actual calculation. When they have finished, they should have an answer to the original problem.

    d. Post-operative evaluation (check the solution). This group checks the answer with the problem to see if it really answers the question.

2. After the procedure has been completed, stress to students that they have just engaged in the four basic steps for problem solving: read, plan, solve, check. Repeat the activity at least three more times with new problems, rotating the groups so that each group gets to participate in all four problem-solving steps.

EXTENSIONS AND ADAPTATIONS

1. A new group could be formed that represents the patient. This group decides what symptoms they have (they develop the actual problem).

2. Related activity Arithme"Tic Tac Toe" on page 133.

VII

CONSUMER
PROBLEM
SITUATIONS

LET'S GO OUT TO EAT

PRIMARY CONTENT

- Estimating money amounts to the nearest dollar
- Adding and subtracting money using the proper symbols

PRIOR STUDENT KNOWLEDGE

Rounding skills (to nearest dollar)

PRE-ACTIVITY PREPARATION

Copy reproducibles Menu Sheet (page 142) and Order Sheet (page 143), one copy for each student.

PROCESS SKILLS

Comparing, calculating, estimating, recording

GROUP SIZE

3 students

MATERIALS PER GROUP

- 1 copy of reproducible Menu Sheet for each student
- 1 copy of reproducible Order Sheet for each student

TEACHER INFORMATION

No special teacher information is required.

PROCEDURE

1. Distribute the materials to each group.

2. One member of the group will be the Waiter or Waitress. The other two students will be the Diners.

3. The Waiter/Waitress passes out the menus and each member of the group decides what four items they want to order. The Waiter/Waitress then records for each Diner the items and their cost on the first form on the Diner's Order Sheet.

4. Each Diner checks the cost of each item. Then he/she estimates the total of his/her meal to the nearest dollar, writing that estimate next to Estimated Total on the Order Sheet. The Waiter/Waitress then adds the actual cost of the order and writes that amount next to Actual Total.

5. Each student then compares the estimate with the actual cost by finding the difference.

6. Repeat the activity two more times so that each student gets a chance to be the Waiter/Waitress.

7. Stress that during the activity, all amounts should be recorded with dollar signs and decimal points.

EXTENSIONS AND ADAPTATIONS

1. Adapt the activity in the following way. Give one member of the group a set amount of play money ($10 or $20). Tell that member that he/she will be paying for the meals. This member should total the estimates of the members in his/her group and determine whether he/she has enough money.

2. Let students use calculators to check their calculations.

3. Have students complete the activity rounding off to the nearest half dollar.

4. Related activities Box Cars on page 52, Show Those Fingers! on page 68, Wheel of Numbers on page 74, Pets Cost Money on page 144, and Stump 'Em on page 148.

LET'S GO OUT TO EAT

MENU SHEET

Name _____

Dino's Diner MENU

SOUP
Chicken $1.20

Vegetable 1.20

Clam Chowder 1.70

SALAD
Garden $1.70

Greek 1.90

Chicken 2.20

BEVERAGES
Coffee . . . .$.70

Tea .70

Milk 1.00

Soda 1.20

SANDWICHES
Hamburger $2.40

Cheeseburger 2.60

Hot Dog 1.30

Tuna 1.80

Grilled Cheese 1.40

Turkey 1.90

SIDE ORDERS
French Fries—large $1.70

French Fries—small 80

Potato Chips 60

DESSERTS
Apple Pie $2.20

Ice Cream 1.20

Fresh Fruit 1.70

LET'S GO OUT TO EAT

ORDER SHEET

Name

ITEM	COST
1.	
2.	
3.	
4.	
Actual Total	
Estimated Total	

ITEM	COST
1.	
2.	
3.	
4.	
Actual Total	
Estimated Total	

PETS COST MONEY _____

PRIMARY CONTENT
- Solving word problems involving addition and subtraction of money
- Adding and subtracting three-digit numbers, with and without regrouping

PRIOR STUDENT KNOWLEDGE
Addition and subtraction skills with and without regrouping; money skills

PRE-ACTIVITY PREPARATION
1. A day or two prior to the activity, ask each student to bring a stuffed toy animal, or a picture of a pet animal, from home. Try to get as large an assortment as possible.
2. On the day of the activity, place animals and pictures on a table. Label each with a price ranging from $2.00 to $5.00.
3. Copy reproducible Pet Problems (page 146), one copy per student.
4. Using Pet Supplies (page 147) as a guide, write a list on the board showing various pets and associated costs of supplies; or develop a handout of such for each student. If desired, all values can be changed to whole dollars or multiples of 10¢. (Page 147 may be copied and used if desired.)

PROCESS SKILLS
Comparing, calculating, recording

GROUP SIZE
Individual

MATERIALS PER GROUP
- Table of priced stuffed toy animals and/or pet pictures (for whole class)
- 1 copy of reproducible Pet Problems for each student
- Pet supplies price list on board or individual handouts, or 1 copy of reproducible Pet Supplies for each student

TEACHER INFORMATION

No special teacher information is required.

PROCEDURE

1. Distribute the materials, telling students that today they are going shopping for a pet.

2. Tell students that they each have $10 to spend on a pet and pet supplies.

3. Let students go (in small groups) to the class Pet Store where each will choose (but not remove from the table) a favorite pet and a second favorite pet. Students each need to note and record the prices of their selections in questions 1 and 6 on their Pet Problems sheet.

4. After selections have been made, direct students each to complete the rest of the problems on their Pet Problems sheet with the aid of the provided pet supplies price list.

5. Discuss results with the class. Did some questions cause more problems than others? What would be the most expensive pet and supplies? What would be the least expensive pet and supplies?

EXTENSIONS AND ADAPTATIONS

1. Raise or lower prices. You could have students do research at a pet store by getting actual prices of items.

2. Have students write their own pet word problems.

3. Related activities Box Cars on page 52, Show Those Fingers! on page 68, Wheel of Numbers on page 74, Let's Go Out to Eat on page 141, and Stump 'Em on page 148.

PETS COST MONEY

PET PROBLEMS

Name _____

1. My favorite pet is a _____ and it costs $____.____ .

2. I would buy my pet a _____ which costs $____.____
   and a _____ which costs $____.____ .

3. I would spend $____.____ on my pet supplies.

4. My pet and the supplies would cost $____.____ .

5. I would receive $____.____ change from my $10.00.

6. My second choice for a pet is a _____ costing $____.____ .

7. This pet's supplies of _____ and _____
   would cost $____.____ .

8. The difference in the cost of the supplies for these two pets is $____.____ .

9. $____.____ is the cost for both pets.

10. $____.____ is the difference in cost between the two pets I like.

PETS COST MONEY

PET SUPPLIES

PETS	SUPPLIES
DOG	1. canned dog food — $.52
	2. flea collar — $1.26
	3. leash — $3.78
GERBIL	1. cage — $2.95
	2. bag of gerbil food — $3.05
	3. water bottle — $1.37
BIRD	1. cuttlebone — $.89
	2. cage — $3.15
	3. bag of bird feed — $1.24
CAT	1. collar and bell — $1.77
	2. canned cat food — $.48
	3. scratching post — $2.68
TURTLE	1. bowl — $2.10
	2. turtle food — $.33
	3. rock — $.15
FISH	1. tank — $4.95
	2. seaweed — $1.88
	3. fish food — $.95
HAMSTER	1. cage — $3.67
	2. sawdust — $1.59
	3. bag of hamster food — $.75

STUMP 'EM

PRIMARY CONTENT

Solving word problems involving addition and subtraction of money

PRIOR STUDENT KNOWLEDGE

Prior exposure to adding and subtracting dollars and cents

PRE-ACTIVITY PREPARATION

Arrange a class field trip to a local store (hardware, department, toy, grocery, etc.). Or you may collect empty cartons, cans, boxes, etc. from various items (food and/or other) with prices written clearly on the containers. Or you may collect pictures of items from catalogs, circulars, newspapers, etc., with prices written clearly on the pictures.

PROCESS SKILLS

Observing, comparing, calculating, recording, problem solving

GROUP SIZE

Whole class followed by groups of 3–4 students

MATERIALS PER GROUP

- 2 index cards (5 in. x 8 in.) per student
- 1 index card (5 in. x 8 in.) per group

TEACHER INFORMATION

No special teacher information is required.

PROCEDURE

1. Based upon objectives and feasibility considerations, do one of the following (see Pre-Activity Preparation):

   a. Take students on a field trip to a local store. Each student should carry paper and pencil. While there, have each student price any two items, writing down the item names and prices for use in step 2.

   b. Using collected containers with marked prices, set up a classroom store. While students browse (they are not to remove any items unless so desired), they are to write down the names and prices of any two items for use in step 2. If preferred, instead of setting up a class store, item containers can be distributed randomly to students (two per student) for use at their desks.

   c. Randomly distribute pictures of various items with marked prices (two per student) for use in step 2.

2. On their index cards, have students each draw and color a picture of each item they priced. They are also to write the name and the price of the item on the card.

3. Set up groups of 3–4 students. Instruct each group to make up a written problem using all the items on group members' index cards. The problem should involve addition and subtraction. It can include (but is not limited to) the idea that students are given a fixed amount of money and need to determine the amount of change.

4. Each group then makes a problem card, stating the problem on the front and the answer on the back.

5. Have groups exchange cards. After working the problems, groups may check the answers on the backs of the cards. Stress to the groups that peeking at the answer before a solution is arrived at is unacceptable and that any group caught "looking" will be disqualified. Remind students that when working with money or decimals, they must make sure place values are lined up to add or subtract.

6. Bulletin boards may be made using the labeled pictures and word problems following the activity.

EXTENSIONS AND ADAPTATIONS

1. Let groups devise more than one word problem.

2. The class could compete to see which group can solve the most problems. Points could be awarded for each problem solved.

3. Set up a store and a cashier. Have students pick up the items and total their bill before they are checked out by the cashier. (A calculator can be used for checking.)

4. The student purchasing the items estimates the cost, and the cashier calculates the actual amount.

5. Students could use play money to carry out the transactions and receive change.

6. Related activities Box Cars on page 52, Show Those Fingers! on page 68, Wheel of Numbers on page 74, Let's Go Out to Eat on page 141, and Pets Cost Money on page 144.

ANSWER
KEY

ANSWER KEY

Activity 7: A Fraction of an Egg
Fraction Sheet 1 (page 18)

A FRACTION OF AN EGG _____

ACTIVITY **7**

FRACTION SHEET 1

Name_____

1. Complete the table. Write the number of spaces used to make the fractions.

Fraction	Spaces Used
$\frac{1}{12}$	1
$\frac{1}{6}$	2
$\frac{1}{4}$	3
$\frac{1}{3}$	4
$\frac{1}{2}$	6

2. What do you notice about the numerators of the fractions?
   All the numerators are 1.

3. Now look at the denominators and the number of spaces used. What happens to the denominators compared to what happens to the number of spaces used?
   As the denominators get smaller, the number of spaces used gets larger.

4. Look at the egg cartons. What happens to the fraction as the denominator gets larger?
   As the denominator gets larger, the fraction gets smaller.

(18)   © Curriculum Associates, Inc. *Mathematics Activities (KSAM)*

Activity 15: Bad Call
Addition Problems (page 49)

BAD CALL _____

ACTIVITY **15**

ADDITION PROBLEMS

Name_____

Directions: Look at the picture of the umpire. Then solve the problems.

1. What would you get if you added his fingers and hat together? ___ **7**
2. What is the total of his ear added to his left arm? ___ **11**
3. What do you have to add to his left shoulder to get 15? ___ **8**
4. If you add together his hat, right shoulder, and mouth, what do you get? **10**
5. What would all the numbers on his face add up to? ___ **13**
6. How much is an elbow plus an ear plus a mouth plus a left arm? ___ **22**
7. How much is 2 umpire hats? ___ **8**
8. What is the total of his eyes added to his hat? ___ **12**
9. What number is added to his nose to get 6? ___ **6**
10. What is the total of all the numbers on the umpire picture? ___ **45**

© Curriculum Associates, Inc. *Mathematics Activities (KSAM)*   (49)

Activity 7: A Fraction of an Egg
Fraction Sheet 2 (page 19)

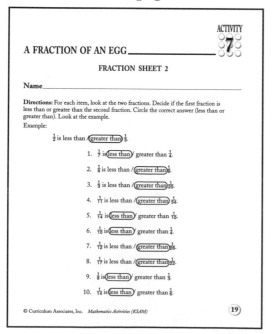

A FRACTION OF AN EGG _____

ACTIVITY **7**

FRACTION SHEET 2

Name_____

Directions: For each item, look at the two fractions. Decide if the first fraction is less than or greater than the second fraction. Circle the correct answer (less than or greater than). Look at the example.

Example:
   $\frac{1}{2}$ is less than /(greater than) $\frac{1}{3}$.

1. $\frac{1}{7}$ is (less than)/ greater than $\frac{1}{4}$.
2. $\frac{1}{6}$ is less than /(greater than) $\frac{1}{8}$.
3. $\frac{1}{3}$ is less than /(greater than) $\frac{1}{26}$.
4. $\frac{1}{11}$ is less than /(greater than) $\frac{1}{34}$.
5. $\frac{1}{14}$ is (less than)/ greater than $\frac{1}{6}$.
6. $\frac{1}{10}$ is (less than)/ greater than $\frac{1}{4}$.
7. $\frac{1}{12}$ is less than /(greater than) $\frac{1}{28}$.
8. $\frac{1}{17}$ is less than /(greater than) $\frac{1}{22}$.
9. $\frac{1}{8}$ is (less than)/ greater than $\frac{1}{3}$.
10. $\frac{1}{14}$ is (less than)/ greater than $\frac{1}{6}$.

© Curriculum Associates, Inc. *Mathematics Activities (KSAM)*   (19)

Activity 15: Bad Call
Subtraction Problems (page 50)

BAD CALL _____

ACTIVITY **15**

SUBTRACTION PROBLEMS

Name_____

Directions: Look at the picture of the umpire. Then solve the problems.

1. What do you get when you subtract the umpire's fingers from his ear? **6**
2. What is the difference between his eyes and his mouth? **3**
3. Take an elbow away from a left shoulder. What do you get? **1**
4. Take a left arm away from an ear. What do you get? **7**
5. Take a nose away from a hat. What do you get? **4**
6. What do you get when you subtract the highest number on the umpire's body and arms from the highest number on his head? **2**

7. ear
    − hat
    _____
    5

8. eyes
    − right shoulder
    _____
    7
    − mouth
    _____
    2

9. mouth
    − left arm
    _____
    3
    − left arm
    _____
    1

10. left shoulder
    − fingers
    _____
    4
    − nose
    _____
    4

(50)   © Curriculum Associates, Inc. *Mathematics Activities (KSAM)*

Activity 15: Bad Call
Multiplication Problems (page 51)

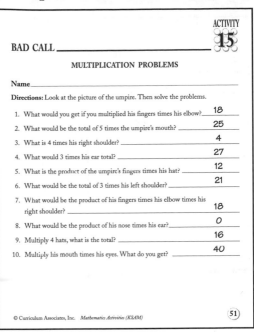

BAD CALL _____ ACTIVITY **15**

MULTIPLICATION PROBLEMS

Name _____

Directions: Look at the picture of the umpire. Then solve the problems.

1. What would you get if you multiplied his fingers times his elbow? ___18___
2. What would be the total of 5 times the umpire's mouth? ___25___
3. What is 4 times his right shoulder? ___4___
4. What would 3 times his ear total? ___27___
5. What is the product of the umpire's fingers times his hat? ___12___
6. What would be the total of 3 times his left shoulder? ___21___
7. What would be the product of his fingers times his elbow times his right shoulder? ___18___
8. What would be the product of his nose times his ear? ___0___
9. Multiply 4 hats, what is the total? ___16___
10. Multiply his mouth times his eyes. What do you get? ___40___

© Curriculum Associates, Inc. *Mathematics Activities (KSAM)* (51)

Activity 28: Measure Up
Metric Measurement (page 91)

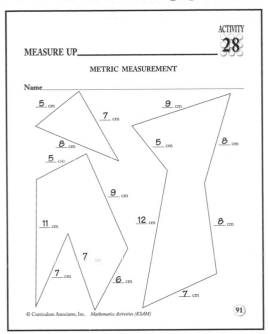

MEASURE UP _____ ACTIVITY **28**

METRIC MEASUREMENT

Name _____

© Curriculum Associates, Inc. *Mathematics Activities (KSAM)* (91)

Activity 28: Measure Up
Customary Measurement (page 90)

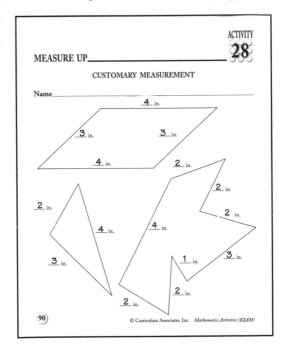

MEASURE UP _____ ACTIVITY **28**

CUSTOMARY MEASUREMENT

Name _____

(90) © Curriculum Associates, Inc. *Mathematics Activities (KSAM)*

Activity 36: Grid It Out
Find Me Grid Sheet (page 123)

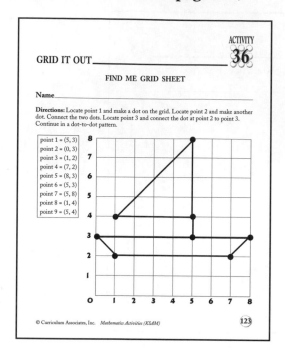

GRID IT OUT_____ ACTIVITY 36

FIND ME GRID SHEET

Name_____

Directions: Locate point 1 and make a dot on the grid. Locate point 2 and make another dot. Connect the two dots. Locate point 3 and connect the dot at point 2 to point 3. Continue in a dot-to-dot pattern.

| point 1 = (5, 3) |
| point 2 = (0, 3) |
| point 3 = (1, 2) |
| point 4 = (7, 2) |
| point 5 = (8, 3) |
| point 6 = (5, 3) |
| point 7 = (5, 8) |
| point 8 = (1, 4) |
| point 9 = (5, 4) |

© Curriculum Associates, Inc.   *Mathematics Activities (KSAM)*   123

Activity 36: Grid It Out
Make a Picture Grid Sheet (page 124)

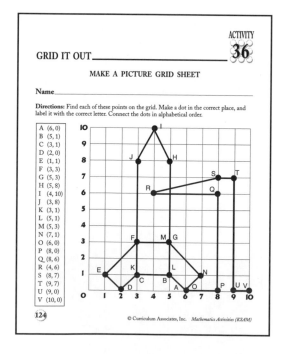

GRID IT OUT_____ ACTIVITY 36

MAKE A PICTURE GRID SHEET

Name_____

Directions: Find each of these points on the grid. Make a dot in the correct place, and label it with the correct letter. Connect the dots in alphabetical order.

| A (6, 0) |
| B (5, 1) |
| C (3, 1) |
| D (2, 0) |
| E (1, 1) |
| F (3, 3) |
| G (5, 3) |
| H (5, 8) |
| I (4, 10) |
| J (3, 8) |
| K (3, 1) |
| L (5, 1) |
| M (5, 3) |
| N (7, 1) |
| O (6, 0) |
| P (8, 0) |
| Q (8, 6) |
| R (4, 6) |
| S (8, 7) |
| T (9, 7) |
| U (9, 0) |
| V (10, 0) |

124   © Curriculum Associates, Inc.   *Mathematics Activities (KSAM)*

Activity 36: Grid It Out
Secret Words Grid Sheet (page 125)

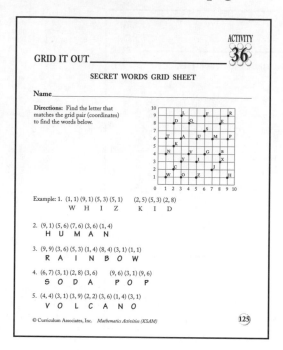

GRID IT OUT_____ ACTIVITY 36

SECRET WORDS GRID SHEET

Name_____

Directions: Find the letter that matches the grid pair (coordinates) to find the words below.

Example: 1. (1, 1) (9, 1) (5, 3) (5, 1)   (2, 5) (5, 3) (2, 8)
W H I Z   K I D

2. (9, 1) (5, 6) (7, 6) (3, 6) (1, 4)
H U M A N

3. (9, 9) (3, 6) (5, 3) (1, 4) (8, 4) (3, 1) (1, 1)
R A I N B O W

4. (6, 7) (3, 1) (2, 8) (3, 6)   (9, 6) (3, 1) (9, 6)
S O D A   P O P

5. (4, 4) (3, 1) (3, 9) (2, 2) (3, 6) (1, 4) (3, 1)
V O L C A N O

© Curriculum Associates, Inc.   *Mathematics Activities (KSAM)*   125

Activity 38: Arithme"Tic Tac Toe"
Tic Tac Toe 1 (page 134)

1. 38	6. 4
2. 60	7. 3
3. 81	8. 77
4. 2	9. 24
5. 6	

APPENDIX A

APPENDIX A

THE MATHEMATICAL PROCESSES

Mathematical process listings may vary depending on the purpose and the degree to which the processes are generalized or detailed. The mathematical process skills and definitions listed below are those utilized in this activity guide. It will be noted that the complexity of the processes increases with higher stages of cognitive development.

A. Processes used at the concrete stage: the physical or mental manipulation of real objects, or suitable pictorial representations, to aid in the development of a concept

    1. Observing   Using all the senses, the direct and indirect examination of materials or phenomena

    2. Comparing   Judging two or more items or observations against each other to assess or determine a characteristic

    3. Sorting   Observing various attributes of elements in a set and grouping them by those qualities

    4. Classifying   Observing the attributes of a given item and placing it in a pre-named or predetermined category according to its qualities

    5. Counting   Determining numerical quantity; answering the question "how many?"

    6. Matching   Pairing elements of a set with elements of a second set, usually in a one-to-one correspondence

    7. Measuring   The process of assigning a number to a physical phenomenon

B. Processes used at the numerical representational stage: skills that apply after a number has been assigned to a quantity or set

    1. Calculating   Using one or more of the basic operations (addition, subtraction, multiplication, and division) to fit a given activity suggested or indicated by the problem; the application of operations to numbers

    2. Estimating   Determining the approximation of a desired answer using the numbers or data available

    3. Averaging   Determining a number that typifies a set of numbers of which it is a function

    4. Gathering   Determining and collecting the relevant numbers to be included in a given set of data

    5. Recording   Making a record of, usually in some sequential order or grouping, gathered data

    6. Graphing   Using some form of a number-line chart to record frequency of each included datum

Mathematics Activities (KSAM)

C. Processes used at the abstract stage: mental processes using reasoning combined with numerical information and/or relevant observations to develop a conclusion or solution

1. Inferring — To make evaluations, draw conclusions, or make deductions based on observations

2. Predicting — To suggest an expected result based upon reason, observations, and inferences

3. Analyzing — Comparing data gathered within the set to determine any classifications or relationships that exist

4. Interpreting — Using analyses of the data to derive meaningful relationships from the data

5. Problem Solving — Completion of a series of steps, which may vary from one problem to another, to determine the solution to a problem; problem solving usually involves recognizing a situation that needs a solution and then applying a strategy or method that results in a resolution based on the available data

APPENDIX B

APPENDIX B

CORRELATION OF ACTIVITIES WITH THE NCTM NATIONAL MATHEMATICS CURRICULUM STANDARDS FOR GRADES K–4

The National Council of Teachers of Mathematics (NCTM) has established a set of national standards in mathematics for all grade levels, K–12, in an effort to improve the quality of school mathematics. The NCTM curriculum standards deal primarily with content priority and emphasis, and they are divided into three categories based upon grade level: K–4, 5–8, and 9–12.

Following is a listing of the NCTM mathematics curriculum standards for grades K–4, the standards category that applies to the activities contained in this guide. The actual correlation of activities with those standards is presented in a table following the listing. In that table, activities are listed in order, and the curriculum standards are identified by number as indicated within the listing. For more detailed information concerning the individual standards, see *Curriculum and Evaluation Standards for School Mathematics* (1989), published by the National Council of Teachers of Mathematics.

NCTM Mathematics Curriculum Standards for Grades K–4

Standard 1. Mathematics as Problem Solving
Standard 2. Mathematics as Communication
Standard 3. Mathematics as Reasoning
Standard 4. Mathematical Connections
Standard 5. Estimation
Standard 6. Number Sense and Numeration
Standard 7. Concepts of Whole Number Operations
Standard 8. Whole Number Computation
Standard 9. Geometry and Spatial Sense
Standard 10. Measurement
Standard 11. Statistics and Probability
Standard 12. Fractions and Decimals
Standard 13. Patterns and Relationships

Mathematics Activities for the Elementary Classroom: Level 2–3

Activity Number and Title	NCTM Mathematics Curriculum Standards for Grades K–4												
	1	2	3	4	5	6	7	8	9	10	11	12	13
1. A Handful of Odds or Evens		●			●	●							
2. Arithmetic Machine	●	●	●			●	●	●					●
3. From Place to Place	●	●				●							
4. The Bigger, the Better	●	●	●			●							●
5. Clowning Around		●				●							
6. Compare and Capture	●	●	●			●							
7. A Fraction of an Egg		●	●			●						●	
8. Skip to My Lou		●		●	●	●	●						●
9. Toss 'Em	●	●	●			●							
10. The Unknown Number	●	●	●			●							
11. Value the Place	●	●				●							
12. Who's on First?	●	●	●	●		●							
13. Mom and Apple Pie	●	●		●		●			●			●	
14. In or Out	●	●	●			●	●	●					●
15. Bad Call	●	●	●			●	●	●					
16. Box Cars	●	●		●		●	●					●	
17. Don't Be a Square	●	●	●			●	●	●					●
18. It's a Snap	●	●	●	●	●	●	●	●		●			●
19. Pick As Many As You Can	●		●			●	●	●					
20. Egg 'Em On	●	●				●	●	●					
21. Show Those Fingers!	●	●				●	●	●					
22. Snip a Grid	●	●	●			●	●	●	●				●
23. Wheel of Numbers	●	●	●			●	●	●				●	
24. Now and Later	●	●	●	●		●	●	●		●			●
25. How Many Pennies Equal a Nickel?	●	●	●	●	●	●				●			●
26. Centi'Me'ter	●	●		●	●	●				●			
27. Face It	●	●	●			●				●			●
28. Measure Up	●	●		●	●	●			●	●			
29. Record a Temp	●	●		●		●				●	●		●

(continues)

(continued)

Activity Number and Title	NCTM Mathematics Curriculum Standards for Grades K–4												
	1	2	3	4	5	6	7	8	9	10	11	12	13
30. Names and Shapes	●	●	●						●				
31. Shape Patterns	●	●	●	●					●				●
32. Pick Your Mind	●	●	●	●		●			●				●
33. Everything's in Shape		●	●	●					●		●		
34. Dots or What?	●	●		●		●			●				●
35. A Hairy Graph	●	●	●	●		●					●		
36. Grid It Out	●	●	●	●		●			●	●			●
37. Mail Delivery	●	●	●	●		●			●	●			●
38. Arithme"Tic Tac Toe"	●	●	●	●		●		●					
39. Operation	●	●	●	●		●	●	●					
40. Let's Go Out to Eat	●	●	●	●	●	●	●	●					
41. Pets Cost Money	●	●	●	●	●	●	●	●					
42. Stump 'Em	●	●	●	●	●	●	●	●					